The Lá

Helen S₁

QUILL AND APPLE PUBLISHING

Quill and Apple Publishing
First Published in 2016
Quill and Apple Publishing
Mayfield
East Sussex

A CIP catalogue record for this book is available from the British Library

Print ISBN: 978-0-9935775-0-5
E pub ISBN: 978-0-9935775-1-2

Illustrations by Sally C Greenfield
Typeset, printed and bound in Great Britain by
Ridgewood Design Ltd, 13 The Nightingales, Uckfield, East Sussex TN22 5ND

DEDICATED TO MY FAMILY, 'THEM INDOORS':
HELEN, BRIAN, ROBERT AND HAZEL.
YOU'RE ALL PAWSOME!

Preface - The Head End!

I wouldn't say I'm opinionated, but I've got a view on most things which I'm not afraid to share. I like to feel I offer a unique perspective on life, from about knee height. Try viewing the world on your hands and knees, preferably not whilst in company otherwise people will talk, and you'll get the general idea. My canine disposition gives me a particular slant on life that is more difficult to share with those not similarly blessed, and this can lead to a few misunderstandings.

Take rabbits for example, my family, who I'll refer to as 'Them Indoors', to protect their anonymity, see them as a nuisance; I see them as an asset. A few years ago, they actually burrowed through from next door, the rabbits not my family that is, and set up home in the corner of the garden, which caused some consternation in the camp. Not for me. How many terriers can boast of ensuite bunnies? I like to employ my natural disposition tactically, to try and help with the preservation of the hardy perennials, but the rabbits seem to have got distinctly quicker over the years, and I rarely catch any now.

Another example of differing viewpoints is illustrated by my preoccupation with rubber balls. 'Them Indoors' don't understand it. I like to have my ball thrown repeatedly, all the time I'm in the garden, but the family are less enthusiastic. When 'Her Indoors' is out watering the garden in the summer, which I assist with, making my little contributions where I can, I follow her round dropping my ball on her feet in the unfailing hope that she'll throw it for me. She grumbles that it's a fixation verging on the clinical, but going back to my original point, that's just a difference of perception. Everyone needs a hobby.

'Them Indoors' don't really comprehend my dislikes either. I would have thought fireworks, the smoke alarm and the Postman were fairly standard subjects for canine displeasure. I've got very sensitive hearing so the first two are obviously uncomfortable. The Postman is more difficult to rationalise, even for me, although I think the shorts may have something to do with it. I also have an irrational fear of carrier bags; they tend to unfurl by themselves which I find rather un-nerving, and I don't like the tray slot in the kitchen next to my bed for the simple reason that 'Her Indoors' tends to over-stack it and things fall out....

There are some dogs I don't like, for example, my nemesis, Gyp the farm dog. As he roams freely across the fields, rounding up sheep, he tends to think of the surrounding lanes as part of his territory too, and takes exception to small, vocal terriers, asserting their right of passage. We never miss an opportunity for a brisk exchange of views, and this adds a certain frisson to my regular perambulations.

Then there's that Red Setter from up the road. I don't know why I dislike him but I just do. 'Her Indoors' is always bemused as I've had a number of Red Setter friends over the years, but she's missing the point. It's not the breed, it's the individual. He doesn't like me much either, but then, in fairness, I think he's learnt that reaction from me. I'm sure he's got a name, it's just that I'm usually barking so loudly that I've yet to hear what it is. I bet he's got a name for me too, probably several actually. Anyway, 'Them Indoors' are allowed to like or dislike people at will, so I don't see why they have a problem with me doing it.

There are some pleasures I share with my family so the variation in viewpoint is more a question of degree. Take food; everyone enjoys it, but it's probably fair to say that my obsession with sourcing it is uniquely mine. 'Them Indoors' might discuss the Ocado order and what to have for tea, but food is my constant preoccupation. I think it's a little interest that I share with most of my breed; some Border Terriers are rather over-weight, so 'Her Indoors' expends a considerable amount of effort on controlling my diet and watching my waistline. It's a constant battle of wits. We're both smart but she's easily distracted, fortunately.

The family's conversance with my particular point of view also varies considerably depending on the family member. 'Her Indoors' is my primary carer and has ultimate responsibility for my well-being. She accompanies me on my walks, serves me my delicate cuisine and imposes her standards on my level of personal hygiene. She deludes herself most of the time that she's trained me, but there are moments where reality imposes itself: I'm my own dog, what can I tell you. She's generally got an uncanny insight into my canine mind and is also fairly patient, but if pushed too far can be quite formidable, so I try not to breach the boundaries of decorum too often.

'Him Indoors' is a reluctant dog owner and his prejudices therefore limit his insightfulness as far as I'm concerned. He never wanted a dog in the first place; nasty insanitary creatures that cause inconvenience, cost money, pong a bit and shed hair and dirt in equal measure. After ten years of dog ownership, he will when pushed, grudgingly admit that he's quite fond of me, but there is a significant caveat to his affection. He likes me when I'm being companionable or entertaining; he doesn't like me when I'm doing anything vaguely dog-like, particularly if that involves bodily fluids or emissions of any kind.

'Junior Her' on the other hand, is my staunchest supporter. She achieved the near impossible feat of masterminding my acquisition, and has always looked out for my well-being, offering the most optimistic interpretation of my actions and championing my cause when I'm in trouble, which is fairly frequently. She taught me to read when I was a puppy. She mistook chewing the books as a sign of indifference, but I was taking it all in. It's a skill that's stood me in good stead. The only time I displease her is when my terrier nature impinges on the well-being of other creatures, furry or feathered. It's best to stay on her good side as

3

she overseas my wardrobe. I'm not sure Gyp the farm dog has ever got over seeing me in a pastel striped scarf with pom-poms on the ends, but that was some time ago, when 'Junior Her' was just a girl.

'Junior Him' is away at university some of the time, although he still seems to spend a remarkable amount of time at home where I think he sees me as part of the general domestic set-up. He keeps unpredictable hours, has no sense of routine, forgets to feed me or let me out, and refuses point blank to clear up my little offerings. On the plus side, he's taught me everything I know about the Arsenal football team, often with some significant additions to my vocabulary when they're playing matches. He also brings home some interesting friends who make a fuss of me, particularly the pretty female ones that he seems to favour. He is also the source of illicit treats. He introduced me to jelly for example.

With such an assorted family, variations of perception is obviously a key issue and I have a strong need to assert my canine identity, improve communications and make my voice heard against the background whimpering of the wider world. I'm already a blogger, if you'll excuse the language, and, unusually for dogs, who normally woof, I also tweet. In addition, I have a regular magazine column, but I feel the need to expand my creative endeavours into a broader literary medium. A book feels an appropriate form in which to share my view of life and breach the void of misunderstanding; after all, I'm a literary kind of dog. They say that everyone has book inside them, although for some frankly, that's where it should stay, but I'm a firm believer in 'better out than in' so watch out; here comes my year from my own, distinctive perspective.

4

chapter one – January

Well, it was the usual lack lustre New Year celebrations. It's always a toss-up for 'Them Indoors' between forgetting the whole thing and going to bed at the usual time or forcing themselves to stay awake and watch the fireworks in London on the TV whilst wishing each other a tepid 'Happy New Year'. My contribution is to bark at the fireworks, whether on the TV or not, and to stagger into the back garden for the nightly ablutions, rather later than usual, without too much reluctance.

Anyway, it won't be long before the indoor tree goes back outdoors, the malevolent twiggy reindeer in the hall that's been giving me the evil eye for the past three weeks, goes back in the loft where he belongs, and I lose the red coat with the white fur trim that makes me look like an animated Christmas decoration when out for my walks. Although I enjoy Christmas, there's a limit to how many turkey left-overs and novelty chews a small dog can consume without it having an adverse effect on the digestion. With all those visitors to greet, presents to unwrap and crackers and

5

party poppers to bark at in case they're fireworks, I am, quite frankly, exhausted, and ready to return to normality, or what passes for it with 'Them Indoors'.

5TH JANUARY - OUT WITH THE OLD

Most people greet the New Year by putting the decorations away and buying a bunch of flowers to cheer the place up, but what does 'Her Indoors' decide to do – wash the dog instead. I'm not sure that 'out with the old and in with the new' usually refers to bath water, but then 'Her Indoors' is a little idiosyncratic. I should have seen it coming. I was sitting by 'Him Indoors' as he was preparing lunch, hoping to get a bit of cheese, when he muttered something about 'whiffy' and 'dog'. Before I could plan evasive action I was whisked upstairs and dunked in the baby bath with a liberal application of shampoo. I'm a terrier; I don't do water. My bedding, collar, harness and coat went into the washing machine. I really think that it's only a matter of time before she puts me in on a hot wash with a biological liquid-tab and disinfectant instead of fabric softener. Anyway, the rubbing down with a soft, warm towel is always pleasant, although I'm not sure that pink is really my colour, and I do get a quick glimpse of the upstairs of the house which is normally out of bounds. True, I'm fluffy in places no self respecting terrier should be fluffy in and I smell like a French Poodle (no offence) but I get lots of fuss and positive comment about the improvement so it's not all bad. It's just a shame it's the winter and I can't go out in the garden and roll in something.

7TH JANUARY - A WHITE WORLD

It's happened again. One minute it's a normal, if slightly dreary January landscape, with muted colours and leaden skies, then you wake up and it's suddenly reverted to black and white. When I was a young dog, we hardly ever had snow in this part of the world, but over the years it's become an increasingly regular occurrence. To be honest, I have mixed feelings about it. Snow holds scent really well so it's exciting trying to piece together the events of the night before, over the playing fields, if 'Them Indoors' will let me sniff for long enough that is, but it's also cold. It's okay for 'Her Indoors' with her water-proof coat and a fleecy liner, two pairs of socks and welly boots, but I've only got the same kit as normal. True, the coat that I had for my birthday comes in very useful, but it doesn't protect the bits not covered in fur. Being a small dog with short legs, I'm beginning to have some sympathy with the brass monkeys.

There are however some mercies. In years gone by 'Junior Him and Her' would insist on taking me sledging which would inevitably involve me being placed on-board and shoved down a slope. There's photographic evidence to prove it should I ever feel the need to contact the RSPCA. Fortunately however, the plastic sledge wasn't designed for the rigours of a six foot two semi-adult, and 'Junior Him' broke it a couple of winters ago. Anyway, he's away at university, so I also avoid the inevitable snow ball throwing. 'Junior Her' wouldn't dream of using me for target practice and 'Her Indoors' wouldn't be able to hit me even if she tried; she throws like a complete girl. I wouldn't entirely put it past 'Him Indoors' though. Still, there are some opportunities for artistic expression. Wee comes out a pleasing shade of yellow against the whiteness of the snow, and I know coal is traditional for snowmen's eyes, but in these environmentally friendly days, I can provide something small, round and brown that's bio-degradable, if required, they don't even have to ask.

Snow has some interesting effects on the norms of everyday life. If it's sufficiently thick, the road outside our house becomes miraculously devoid of traffic. As the pavements are treacherous, we sometimes abandon the pedestrian highways altogether and walk in the tyre tracks on the road. It gives an interesting change of perspective. Then there's the effect on everyone else. People are extra friendly and chat about the weather, how much wood they've got left and the price of heating oil. And there's the dogs. I saw that Red Setter from up the road across the playing fields. He had totally lost his marbles and was frolicking around in the snow, rolling and grabbing mouthfuls of the stuff. I know he's younger than me, but honestly, what a disgraceful lack of canine decorum. Barnie from next door was far more sensible, as I'd expect. He was also wearing a practical coat as he's got short fur, and was very busy indulging his hound nature, following scents. He did pause to say hello, as he's a polite kind of fellow, but he was too preoccupied to stop for long.

12TH JANUARY - MALE BONDING

Well it's back to the usual routine. 'Junior Him' has gone back to university and I rather miss him. He takes after 'Him Indoors' with helping me out in the snacking department, which is handy, and out of all the family, his foot work with a rubber ball is definitely the best. He's honed his skills playing football at university – a marvellous thing education. I don't always understand what people do, but the concept of adults running round a field chasing after a ball is something I can totally identify with. I think 'Junior Him' misses me when he's away as he did mutter something about taking me back with him, but 'Her Indoors' crisply pointed out that dogs need exercise, feeding and a regular routine. I can't argue with that. He seemed to think I might have been able to help with the mouse that popped out of the toaster in his student digs one night, but I'd have been asleep myself. What does he think I am anyway, a cat? Still, he'll soon be back with a bag of interestingly pungent dirty laundry. I gather he's taking a digital photography unit at university with 'animals' as one of the possible subject options. I'd like to help out if I can. Now which is my best side...?

15TH JANUARY - FRIENDS AND FOES

We ventured a little off our normal route this morning. I think 'Her Indoors' is a bit embarrassed by my continued spat with that Red Setter from up the road. It's a bit like a game of chicken, seeing who is going to bark first. We do our ritual exchange of hostilities whilst 'Her Indoors' attempts the usual pleasantries with the other owner – fat chance. Personally, I find all that barking quite invigorating, but 'Her Indoors' mutters grimly under her breath at me and calls me by one of my alternative names.

We couldn't go passed the Farm either, after that little spot of unpleasantness before Christmas when I was ambushed by Gyp the farm dog sneaking up on me along the other side of the hedge. Underhand tactics, but then I'd expect nothing better to be honest. It's just as well there's a good choice of side roads.

I bumped into Dolly, the Highland Terrier from a few doors up, when I was out walking, and she was wearing a lampshade. To begin with I thought it was the latest in doggy accessorising, a bit of a step up from a coat or bandana, but I gather from 'Her Indoors' it had something to do with an ear problem. Dolly might have looked a bit like an angle-poise lamp, but at least it was keeping the rain off.

I also saw Barnie from next door. It's all polite sniffing and tail wagging when we meet. I know who I like and who I don't although 'Her Indoors' hasn't quite got to grips with the politics of dog relationships.

It was a wet walk this morning. 'Her Indoors' always takes her exercising duties very seriously so we go out whatever the weather. Sometimes, if it's very bad, we reach a certain point, take pity on each other, and head for home. Still, it's always fun watching 'Her Indoors' trying to juggle a large golfing umbrella, her gloves and my lead, with picking up my little offerings, particularly if it's windy too. Her language can leave a bit to be desired on those occasions. Not the kind of words you hear on the BBC.

She's a bit smug because she thinks she's mastered the technique of getting me to shake outside the back door. One of her dog owning friends said that the trick is to ruffle my fur up the wrong way so I have to shake to put it back in order. She's right, it works. Still, I always wait until I'm in the comfort of my own home before I give it a proper go – the one outside is just a warm-up. It's amazing how far you can get those muddy droplets to go if you really try. They leave an interesting pattern on the white goods too. Then there's the muddy paw prints. I'm supposed to go straight in my basket when I come back from my walk, but on wet days I favour a little wander around the kitchen before I settle so that I can express my artistic creativity on the tiled floor. 'Her Indoors' doesn't seem to appreciate this and her entreaties to confine myself to my bed get increasingly shrill. If I'm really wet, I get a rub down with kitchen roll in the lobby, which I have to say I rather enjoy – what male wouldn't. If she misses a bit, there's always her trouser legs, particularly once she's changed out of her dog walking jeans, ready for work. Damp days in January – you have to make your own fun.

'Them Indoors' watched a programme about dogs on the TV last night. There were lots of puppies which sent 'Her' and 'Junior Her' into an unnecessary flutter. 'Him Indoors' retained his composure however, and muttered darkly about expense, chewing and incontinence. He's got a long memory, I'll give him that. Anyway, they discovered that dogs don't actually see in black and white as they'd previously thought. We can manage certain colours, but we don't do well with red and orange, which explains why I keep losing my ball. I need one in blue. Apparently, dogs are much more likely to be successful guide dogs if their fur swirls in an anticlockwise direction and they are right pawed. It indicates a biddable, well behaved dog, whereas those who are left pawed with clockwise swirls tend to be independent individuals, likely to come up with unusual solutions and tend to be a bit unpredictable. I'm not much into fur swirls, I'm a Border Terrier with a rough working coat for goodness sake, but guess which category I fall into in the paw department? That's my alternative career path terminated then. 'Him and Her Indoors' came and cajoled me out of my bed so that they could check which paw I moved first when walking. They had already correctly guessed of course. Still, at least they understand better why the smoke alarm is so painful to me and what evolutionary gems we dogs really are. The TV can be useful. It's not all Jeremy Kyle and EastEnders after all.

25TH JANUARY - FOOD FOR THOUGHT

The cold weather makes me feel a bit peckish so I did a bit of 'self-service' on my walk this morning. I managed to find all kinds of stuff up the playing fields to have a chew on. I employed my usual 'all grist to the mill' policy, but 'Her Indoors' got so cross she put me back on the lead to reduce my resourcing potential. Honestly, you'd think she'd be pleased. Recycling is very environmentally friendly.

I felt a bit unwell this afternoon. I sat by the back door for a while waiting for someone to notice and let me out, but nothing happened so I was sick on the mat. 'Her Indoors' wasn't best pleased when she came in from work. She has some very pungent floor cleaner in a squeezy bottle under the sink, kept handy for such emergencies, and it's a smell that I associate with being in disgrace. It's just as well 'Him Indoors' wasn't around otherwise he wouldn't have spoken to me for a week. 'Her Indoors' wisely didn't tell him when he came in from work. It's one of those little omissions, like not mentioning clothing sale purchases, that help to smooth the path of long relationships and avoid any unnecessary conflict. I'm all for side-stepping unpleasantness myself, particularly when I'm the subject of it.

Anyway, I've had to revert to seeking food by more traditional means. 'Him Indoors' usually gives me my breakfast. He has his own first; something to do with the pack pecking order – he's been reading those dog psychology books again. Then he goes and gets the tin of biscuits and I sit patiently watching as he finds one of each sort and places them in my bowl for me. 'Her Indoors' once caught him explaining to me what each of the different coloured biscuits are supposed to do. The orange ones give you a shiny coat, the brown ones give you energy, the pale ones give you strong bones and the black ones are supposed to deal with flatulence. 'Him Indoors' got quite a bit of teasing over that but I thought it was rather considerate of him.

One morning 'Her Indoors' burst the cereal packet and scattered half a packet all over the floor. I was there like a shot I can tell you. I didn't reckon it very much though. The bran flakes were a bit dry and bland, whilst the sultanas were tasty but got stuck round my teeth. I'd rather have my biscuits. Still, it kept me going all day.

When 'Him Indoors' is away on business, 'Her Indoors' has to do the early shift and feed me. Sometimes she forgets though; she isn't at her brightest and best first thing. I think it might have been Jean Paul Sartre who said 'Hell is other people at breakfast' and that's a view I suspect 'Her Indoors' would agree with. Anyway, I have to do lots of sitting around looking hungry and staring pointedly at my bowl, resorting to pathetic whimpering as a last resort.

There is an upside however. Occasionally, if I play my cards right, I can get two breakfasts when 'Him Indoors' is away. 'Junior Her' knows that her Mum is a bit unreliable, and if 'Her Indoors' has gone into the bathroom and isn't available for consultation, I try my hungry eyes. Sometimes I do it so well that 'Junior Her' assumes I haven't been fed and gives me a second go, which I eat with the same relish as the first so that she doesn't suspect anything. I usually get found out eventually, and then 'Her Indoors' indulges in some unseemly name calling which is, quite frankly, beneath her, but by then it's too late and I have the last laugh.

30TH JANUARY - HORSING AROUND

I've always had a bit of a thing about horses; large clippy-cloppy and frankly rather alarming, although quite impressive in the poohing department. Anyway, my unrestrained vocal rebuke of anything vaguely equestrian, upsets 'Her Indoors'. I think she's worried I'll be responsible for unseating a rider, although the nearest we've come to that was an unfortunate incident when 'Her Indoors' unfurled her golfing umbrella at an inopportune moment.

However, having identified a training need, 'Her Indoors' has been remarkably persistent. I made sure it took a long time and lots of treats before I caught on to what was expected. I get generous praise from the riders who know me by name due to 'Her Indoors' scolding me when I succumb to temptation. They've no idea who she is of course. There's one horse, who's accompanied by a free roaming Border Collie, that I have particular difficulty in not barking at. It's probably because the dog reminds me a bit of Gyp the farm dog. I've just about managed to restrain myself these days, aided by copious bribery treats from 'Her Indoors', but the horse has got a long memory and gets a bit nervous when he sees me. He does lots of that trotting sideways and backing up the lane, showing the whites of his eyes. It looks all the more ridiculous because he is a big horse, and I'm a rather small dog. Anyway, I caught his name for the first time this morning – Hercules – you've just got to laugh!

Chapter Two - February

1ST FEBRUARY - FRACTIOUS FARM DOGS

I ventured past the farm today which we haven't done in a while. As we got close, there was a lot of barking, and I got my hopes up of a rousing altercation with my arch-enemy, Gyp the farm dog, but as we got closer it turned out just to be Hobo and Frank, the farm Jack Russells. They started off barking at me but ended up having a go at each other. Poor old Frank. Hobo's a bit of a young upstart. He looks cute enough with curly fur, like he's had a bad perm, but he's a pugnacious little fellow. Still, they're both ok, after all, they're terriers. Just as I'd given up hope of a proper fractious encounter, I spotted Gyp the farm dog with Debbie the farmer, further along the lane. Debbie wasn't taking any risks and Gyp was bundled into the back of the Land Rover quicker than you can say 'flying fur'. 'Her Indoors' was very strict with me too, so there was little opportunity for an exchange of hostilities. I did however manage a quick woof as we walked past. Gyp tried to reciprocate but Debbie banged on the side of the Land Rover and shouted at him (no less than Gyp deserved) so that was the end of that. Spoilsports.

7TH FEBRUARY - OFSTED AND OFF ABROAD

Well it's been a bit of a week. 'Him Indoors' disappeared off to Boston and narrowly avoided being trapped there by an imminent blizzard, swapping last minute to an earlier flight, whilst 'Her Indoors' has had Ofsted in at work so sightings of her have been rare and fleeting. When she has been at home she's been a bit pre-occupied, muttering about retention, attendance and success rates whilst reading feverishly through piles of paperwork. Still, it all ended yesterday when she subsided into a comfortable chair in front of the woodburner with two large glasses of wine, a Cadbury's Creme Egg, and a chick flick which she watched with 'Junior Her'.

I'm not sure if Ofsted realise what sacrifices I've made this week and what a crucial role I've played in the inspection process. My walks have been sadly curtailed and I've had to rely on 'Junior Her' for most of my needs. I tried to distract 'Her Indoors' by misbehaving due to all that pent up energy, and presenting her with a toy rather pointedly whenever she ventured into the kitchen, just to make it plain that I was being a bit neglected, but I don't think it even registered. Still, 'Junior Her' stepped up to the mark pretty well, and it's the price we all have to pay for a good adult education service.

10TH FEBRUARY - FURRY MISCREANTS

'Them Indoors' are being bothered by a host of furry pests, not including myself of course. They've had the usual rural winter problem of mice in the loft, which 'Him Indoors' deals with swiftly and efficiently using conventional traps bated with peanut butter. Outside, the rabbits are still very much in evidence, much to the distress of 'Her Indoors', as they eat her plants. I've tried to help a bit on that score, but my hit rate would definitely stand improvement. The other problem is that rabbits are most active in the early morning. 'Her Indoors' has tried to get me out of bed at the crack of dawn to chase them but I'm not playing that game. Who does she think I am – Gyp the farm dog? I'm a pet not a working dog. I need my beauty sleep.

On the rare occasion I do succeed in catching a rabbit, I place 'Her Indoors' in a real dilemma. She doesn't like the rabbits because of the horticultural carnage they cause, but they're cute and furry, qualities I personally rely on as well to keep me out of trouble. She doesn't know whether to praise me or scold me, so we usually share an embarrassed silence whilst she gets a carrier bag and disposes of the evidence. I don't know why she worries, there's plenty more where they came from; they breed like rabbits.

Another species of annoying furry animal are the moles. The slightest sign of them and 'Him Indoors' loses all sense of proportion and starts to rant. Sometimes, when he's indoors, he'll see a mole hill coming up and he rushes out, stabbing at the ground with his garden fork like a man possessed. He's never managed to get one of course. I've tried to help by weeing on the mole hills but that doesn't seem to discourage them either. 'Her Indoors' has persuaded 'Him' that he needs to call the mole man out straight away otherwise the moles dig a network of tunnels that other moles can move into, but secretly I think she just can't stand all the moaning and swearing. Still, the mole man came out last week. He sets traps and leaves the sticks poking up to mark the spot. 'Her Indoors' keeps a sharp eye out in case I try pulling the sticks out to chew on. I must admit I do find the whole process rather intriguing with the thought of those little furry creatures under our very feet. The mole man caught two yesterday, so peace and tranquillity have been restored until the next mole hill appears.

Our neighbour has suggested that moles don't like those plastic children's windmills that catch the breeze, so 'Her Indoors' has planted a line of them along the hedge next to the field where the

17

moles come from. It looks like a miniature wind farm. All they need to do now is connect them up to the National Grid and they'll fund the cost of the mole man. Still, it should at least make them realise that although I've got fur, I'm actually no trouble at all.

12TH FEBRUARY - STICKS AND STONES.......
'Junior Him' is back from university for the weekend to warm up, have a few square meals and get his laundry done for him. I'm not sure where he frequents when he's away from home, but he did say that it was nice to see a terrier that wasn't a Pit Bull......

One of the good things about 'Junior Him' is that he usually refers to me by my proper name, Rolo. It's a nice name although I did temporarily go off it when I bumped into a cat at the Vets with the same appellation. 'Him Indoors' swears I was named after a Viking chief, whilst 'Her Indoors' thinks I was named after the sweet and the fact that I was the last puppy left in the litter not chosen. I think I prefer the idea of being named after a sweet actually. Anyway, whatever the true history, I seem to get called anything but. Here's a quick selection of some of the more well-worn alternative names:

Maximum – Short for 'maximum affront to the senses', originating with and used by 'Him Indoors' (does he think I have no feelings?).

Minimum – A small dog with a big personality, also used by 'Him Indoors'.

Mutley – Something to do with an old children's cartoon called 'Catch the Pigeon'. Rather appropriate as I don't like pigeons either. Used by 'Her Indoors'.

Dog–Dog – I was once so called by a very small child with a limited vocabulary. Factual (although there's actually only one of me, I can understand why he might have thought otherwise), but unimaginative. Anyway, it seems to have stuck with 'Her Indoors'.

Old Flea Bag – Another one used by 'Him Indoors', usually when I'm caught scratching. Sometimes preceded by the word 'pongy', whiffy' or 'smelly' which is usually an early warning sign that a bath is imminent.

Fortesque Bottomly Smythe – Invented by 'Him Indoors' whose mental machinations are a complete mystery to me. The name is often abbreviated to 'Bottomly'. I can't think why.

Gorgeous Boy – Only ever used by 'Junior Her', my staunchest supporter, bless her.

Darling Boy – Also used by 'Junior Her' and 'Her Indoors' during our more intimate, tummy tickling, falling asleep on a lap in front of the wood burner, moments

That Bl***y Dog – Usually favoured by 'Him Indoors' who, when he's seriously annoyed, prefaces it with 'Your'. Very occasionally, and only in extremis, it's used by 'Her Indoors' which basically means putting Battersea Dogs' Home on standby and calling in 'Junior Her' to plead mitigation, I'm in serious trouble.

They do sometimes call me Rolo, but usually only when they want me to do something, as in 'Rolo, come!' and 'Rolo, sit!'. I usually ignore them. That'll teach them to indulge in name-calling.

12TH FEBRUARY - SHOVE TUESDAY

There are certain times of the year where food is central to what is going on, and Pancake Day is one of them. It's supposed to be about finishing the leftovers before fasting over Lent, but the fasting bit has been quietly forgotten and it's the pancakes that have become the key thing. Anyway, 'Her Indoors' usually makes the batter and 'Him Indoors' generally fries them. They're not very adventurous and turn them over with a spatula, however this year 'Junior Her' persuaded 'Him' to give the traditional tossing technique a go. Now I really didn't mean to barge into him at the crucial moment, but I have to admit the pancake on the kitchen floor was delicious. The only disadvantage was that it hadn't yet been smothered with golden syrup or lemon and sugar, which was a shame. Still, I'll work on my timing for next year. No-one can say I'm lacking in ambition.

14TH FEBRUARY - CUPID CYNIC

Call me an old cynic, but I'm not sure I buy into all this Valentine's Day nonsense. Take 'Him' and 'Her Indoors' for example, they've been married for about a hundred years, know each other inside out, yet they still indulge in cards that are supposed to be from secret sweethearts, flowers chocolates etc. I can't say I blame 'Him Indoors', he's obviously hopeful, but with me around, there's no chance. I'm not saying I'm a jealous dog, but what are they doing trying to hug each other when they've got me to lavish their affections on? Should they try any of that nonsense in my presence, I nudge my way in between them and make my rightful claim for a share of the affection. Having had a little operation when I was barely out of adolescence, and when even the curtains seemed a promising bet, I can't quite recall what it's all about anyway. I occasionally have an urge to embrace the leg of 'Him Indoors' rather tightly, which always seems to provoke an embarrassed annoyance from 'Him' and much amusement from 'Her', but I'm not sure what all the fuss is about myself. To mix metaphors, Cupid, bar Humbug!

16TH FEBRUARY - SQUIRRELING AWAY

It must be the milder weather after the cold snap, but there were a lot of squirrels around on my walk this morning. Annoying creatures. They chase around in the upper branches, flaunting the fact that they're flagrantly out of reach, flicking their tails and making chattering noises. I usually bark at them in an attempt to scare one into falling out of a tree, but so far it isn't working.

I very nearly caught one once however, and it's a moment I often relive in my dreams. The cunning little blighter who visits our garden had worked out that I was normally only at large when 'Them Indoors' were outside too. They've got trust issues and don't tend to leave me outside on my own – I can't think why. Anyway, on one particularly sunny day, I had fallen asleep on the lawn, so 'Her Indoors' took pity and left me when she went inside. The squirrel saw 'Her Indoors' go and thought he was safe to run across the lawn. He got half way, into no-man's land, before he realised his mistake. I awoke from my slumbers and had him there, squarely in my sights. I thought I must be still dreaming! I tore across the lawn like Usaine Bolt, but the squirrel, realising the mortal danger he was in, really shifted and managed to get to the Silver Birch a micro-second before me. I flung myself up the tree and was so close I could feel the fluff on his tail, but I just missed. I knew I wasn't dreaming then – If I had been, I'd have got him. Still, although he's now learnt to be even more cautious, I've also learnt a lesson: never give up hope.

18TH FEBRUARY - LOCAL DOGS

One of the things I like about living in a village is the tight-knit community of other dogs. Almost every family seems to own at least one. We've got neighbouring dogs and a dog over the road, Bouncing Betty the Boxer, whose back garden sides onto the playing field. Her owners have thoughtfully provided her with a chain link fence so that she can see all the other dogs visiting the field. She bounces next to the fence barking. She must jump a good five feet in the air – very impressive – and I've been making a careful observation of her technique.

When I got home from my walk today, 'Her Indoors' made herself a sandwich for her packed lunch and accidentally dropped a piece of Waitrose sliced chicken breast on the floor. It was delicious so I tried a Betty bounce next to the work top to see if I could get some more. All I got was thoroughly told off.

Me and 'Her Indoors' have bumped into an old dog over the playing fields several times recently. She's greying and a bit stiff legged (the dog, not 'Her Indoors, although saying that...) but she seems a good sort. Anyway, 'Her Indoors' correctly managed to identify the breed combination as a Labrador/Border Collie cross so she was all pleased with herself. I don't know why, particularly, as we've known a number of dogs of that disposition over the years. Anyway, apparently the dog's thirteen so she's got a few years on me. She's generally quite slow although I was pretty impressed with the sudden turn of speed she developed when she spotted a crisp packet blowing about. She had her nose in there quicker than you could say Border Terrier. Still, she kindly vacated and I was able to take a turn myself. As I'm somewhat smaller, I managed to get my whole head in the packet and explore the corners before 'Her Indoors' caught up with me and took it away. Spoilsport. An owner chat on greedy dogs ensued. Apparently Labradors are very food focused too and will eat almost anything. This was not really news to me. One of my 'Dogs-in-Law' Archie, a Labrador, once ate a whole light bulb. He was whisked to the Vet who gave him something to ease its passage, but he came to no harm. It's a pretty impressive achievement though. Quite illuminating in fact!

Another dog I see occasionally is the smallest dog in the village. He's a Pomeranian and I'm not sure of his name but he's a chirpy little thing, trotting gamely along at the end of his lead like an animated pom-pom. His owner always reels him in when she sees me which is a bit of a shame as I'm sure we could be friends. He'd be a useful ally as he'd be able to fit into all the places I'm too big for. Perhaps his owner worries that I'll mistake him for a rabbit. As if! I know another dog when I see one, even if he is very small.

Apparently Gyp the farm dog made that mistake one day and only a last minute realisation on his part prevented an unfortunate incident. It's not, in fairness, that Gyp is unintelligent, I just think he spends a bit too much time with sheep.

21ST FEBRUARY - BARKING BACK

The sun has been out so I've spent a good part of the day out in the garden which is what I like doing best. The only downside to this is the noise restrictions. Now I'm a fairly vocal dog, it's got to be said, and there's always so much to comment on. There was Bouncing Betty from over the road doing a fair bit of woofing herself. It would have been rude not to reply. Then there's Charlie from next door. He's getting on a bit, and to be honest doesn't hear as well as he used to, but I like to exchange a few pleasantries with him through the hedge. Barnie next door on the other side, is generally too quiet a dog for any useful dialogue, although we have the odd moment, but that still leaves crows flying overhead, squirrels, rabbits, horses clip-clopping along the road and then just a bit of barking for the fun of it. There's never a dull moment. The only problem is, 'Them Indoors' don't like it and imposed a ban on excessive barking some time ago. If I transgress, I get sent inside with a sharp scolding. I've tried barking with a ball in my mouth in the hope that this doesn't count, but apparently it does. 'Junior Her' does her level best and told 'Her Indoors' that if they didn't want a barking dog they shouldn't have bought a terrier. She also pointed out that barking was my natural means of communication and that it was unfair to inhibit my free expression. 'Her Indoors' was a bit taken aback, but I think 'Junior Her' made a good case. I wonder if she's considered becoming a lawyer? Anyway, sometimes I just go for it and live with the consequences. They usually relent and let me back outside after a bit again. I try my best and it's all good fun.

We've finally got to the end of February, a mercifully short month. That's the worst two of the year over with then. There's not really much to recommend January and February. The weather's poor, summer barbeques are a distant memory and the days are short. Still, there are a few compensations and the woodburner is definitely one of them. 'Them Indoors' don't allow me unfettered access to the whole of the house. I can't think why. There's a children's stair gate in the doorway to the kitchen which I could probably jump over if I tried, but usually I'm not that bothered. I've got my bed in the kitchen, a nice warm radiator for me to lean against, plus I'm in the hub of the house, where people congregate and all the food is prepared. Why would I want to be anywhere else? Until the woodburner is lit that is. I can smell it, so I'm there like a shot, sitting by the gate whimpering. 'Them Indoors' usually take pity and let me in. I don't just settle for lying on the floor either. Someone's lap is a much better option. It was a habit developed in my puppyhood when I was small and cute, but I can still just about fit on, although I struggle a bit with 'Junior Her'. There's additional warmth on a lap, and the option of tummy tickling. If my snoring or bodily emissions get a bit too much, I'm passed around between family members and I occasionally take it upon myself to swap laps, just to add a bit of variety, but there's nothing nicer than lying in front of a roaring fire, watching the flames dance. Sometimes it gets a bit warm and I have to pant which usually leads to complaints of dog's breath (what other sort am I supposed to have?), but I pride myself on never giving up and retreating to the kitchen. It gives a whole new meaning to the phrase 'hot dog'.

chapter Three - March

Well they say that March comes in like a lion and goes out like a lamb, the latter part of which is fairly accurate around here as the lambs usually arrive around Easter time. I know is the bad weather makes 'Her Indoors' grumpy. She really can't cope with an umbrella, gloves, pooh bags and a retractable dog lead all at the same time. She dropped her new gloves in the mud; that was my fault. The umbrella blew inside out; that was my fault. We had a slight misunderstanding about which direction I was going in and she dropped the extendable dog lead. It retracted through the mud and hit me up the jack-see; that was my fault too apparently, in spite of me being the injured party. Worst of all, one of the pooh bags had a hole in it which she didn't notice. I'm not going to elaborate, but suffice to say, a lot of tissues were involved. How could that have possibly been my fault?

Anyway, this blame culture is taking its toll on my normal positivity and I think I might be suffering from a touch of Seasonal Affective Disorder. It doesn't help that I'm slightly vertically challenged and cannot see out of the kitchen window and appraise the state of the weather before I emerge into it. Every morning I wait at the back door whilst 'Her Indoors' puts on her copious layers, then I charge outside full of hope and anticipation, only to be met by a sheet of the wet stuff. It's not only the spirits that are dampened I can tell you.

It didn't help matters when 'Him Indoors' announced that I was smelling of dog (what else am I supposed to smell of?) and I found myself back in the baby bath, being lathered up. My last bath was only at Christmas so the frequency of such ablutions is getting frankly worrying. And it's not as if I've been short of the odd shower or two; it's been raining for months.

Still, 'Her Indoors' tried to cheer me up with some home-made dog biscuits. I have to say they were delicious. 'Junior Him' popped back for the weekend and I'm not sure if he realised it, but those 'bow shaped' savoury biscuits he was tucking into happily last night, were actually my dog biscuits in the shape of bones. I notice 'Him and Her Indoors' helped themselves to quite a few as well. Bloomin' cheek! I'm not allowed to eat theirs so this sharing business seems to be a bit of a one way street.

5TH MARCH – SICK AS A DOG
I've had a rather grim few days. I picked up a stomach bug which decided to manifest itself whilst 'Her Indoors' was at work, betraying me at both ends. She came back to a heavily decorated kitchen floor and a rather pungent aroma. Even I was finding it a bit much. She tried not to be cross with me, as it clearly wasn't my fault, although she did mutter under her breath about me eating stuff in the garden. I can't help it if I'm permanently peckish. It's a burden we Border Terriers have to bear. Anyway, there was barely space for her to carefully place her feet. She had to clear

up with kitchen roll, kitchen floor wipes, then wash the floor with a cloth and water in a bucket, followed by a floor steam clean with one of those fancy new floor steamers. Mind you, as she pointed out rather darkly, there was one thing to be thankful for: 'Him Indoors' wasn't around otherwise we'd have both had him to contend with too. As it was it took all my charm to get much in the way of sympathy when he came home from work.

We were away at the weekend, visiting the parents of 'Her Indoors'. I usually enjoy these little trips as 'the Grandies' used to have a dog and enjoy a bit of canine company. However, on this occasion I was decidedly out of sorts. I felt so ill and disorientated that I howled all night, much to the consternation of 'Her Indoors'. The first night she made frequent visits to reassure me, but last night she gave in and we spent a cosy night in the living room with 'Her Indoors' sleeping on the sofa and me on the floor next to her. 'Her Indoor' is a bit weary today – I can't think why. Anyway, I felt much better but was overwhelmed with hunger. I found a box of 'After Eight' mints on the lower shelf of a consul table, but one of 'the Grandies' discovered me as I was trying to break through the cellophane, and confiscated them which was a shame.

Unfortunately, in all the disruption caused by my being ill, I let slip that I can count. It's usually wise to underplay the whole intelligence thing as new opportunities present themselves if they think you're not that bright. Anyway, after days of starvation, 'Him Indoors' tentatively gave me my breakfast biscuits but only gave me three instead of my usual five. I was so shocked I couldn't help but communicate this to 'Him Indoors'. He seemed quite surprised, so I've obviously fooled him previously. 'Her Indoors' wasn't surprised at all, she just smiled knowingly. She's definitely got the measure of me which is a bit worrying. I shall have to keep this in mind now I'm back to regular.

Another Crufts' champion graced our TV screens with their glossy coat and show-dog trotting. It was a nice dog but it's a shame it wasn't a Border Terrier. 'Her Indoors' and 'Junior Her' went to Crufts one year. They didn't win anything! They chose the terrier and hound day so they saw lots of great dogs. Apparently, none of the other Border Terriers compared favourably with me, but they did fall in love with an Irish Wolf Hound. They gave it some thought but concluded that it wouldn't fit in the kitchen and that 'Him Indoors' would probably leave home. He's never been that keen on canines and an Irish Wolf Hound is rather a lot of dog. It's a bit of a shame as I quite fancy having one as a friend. It would be like having a minder. One of the breeders they got talking to owns a Jack Russell as well as her Irish Wolf Hound and apparently the small dog is definitely the boss. Quite right too.

The mini agility was quite good to watch on the TV and there was a lean, toned Border Terrier doing their stuff, I'm pleased to report. I can bark a lot too so I could take part. I like to think I would have been good at the active bit too, when I was younger. There was one canine doing rather nicely, weaving in and out of the poles, when they decided to stop and answer the call of nature, much to the detriment of their chances of winning. It's good to see the dogs aren't taking it that seriously anyway. The Miniature Poodles were very agile too so I barked at them, just to show I'm not partisan. There's more to Poodles than fancy hair that's for sure. Which reminds me of an old joke – How can you tell if it's raining cats and dogs? You step in a Poodle.......

I know Crufts has attracted a bit of controversy over the years. As a pedigree dog myself (yes, I like to think I hide it well), from a long line of distinguished Border Terriers, I have to say that buying a known breed has the advantage of giving you a fair idea of what you're getting , unless they happen to be left pawed with clockwise fur swirls of course. I do think however, that the dog's health and well-being should be at the very centre of any breed standard. Flat faces, big eyes, folds of skin and long backs are all fine, provided they don't cause the dog any issues. If they do, they should just adjust the breed standard so they're not such extreme features. Cross-breeds are fine too; I've know quite a few over the years and it's always fun trying to identify the mix. In fact most dogs are fine with me, unless I don't like them and that's got nothing to do with breed and everything to do with the cut of their jib, just ask that Red Setter from up the road.

I've never been in a dog show. They hold a fun show every year, as part of the village summer fair, but 'Her Indoors' won't enter me, muttering something about not wanting to be humiliated in public. They have a class for the sprightliest senior which I'd surely have a chance of winning. There's a class for the waggiest tail, the brightest eyes, and the quickest retrieval of a rubber ball. I fancy wining a rosette. I would have it above my bed in the kitchen so that all our guests would be in no doubt about the class of dog they were visiting. I think I'll have to work on 'Her Indoors'. I've always enjoyed an audience which is probably what she's worried about......

22ND MARCH – PEOPLE TRAINING

Over the years I've acquired a wealth of experience and I sometimes feel the urge to pass on my knowledge to the younger generation so that they can cut a few corners. One of my areas of expertise is in people training, and I'm wondering if I should hold classes. Most dogs manage to train their immediate family and I'm no exception with 'Them Indoors', although I think 'Him Indoors' has been a particular achievement bearing in mind his oft quoted mantra on dogs: unhygienic creatures who pong a bit and share their hair, bodily emissions and vocals to the detriment of mankind, particularly 'Him Indoors'. In spite of this, I've still managed to train him in the regular sharing of snacks when 'Her Indoors' isn't looking; it's a kind of male conspiracy.

'Her Indoors' doesn't stand any nonsense but she has a soft heart which can be useful. Sometimes, when I've been out in the garden, I forget to bring my ball back into the house with me. When I want to play later, I get quite upset if I can't find it and 'Her Indoors' has been known to don her coat and welly boots, in inclement weather, to find my ball for me and ease my distress. How's that for training?

My greatest achievements however, have involved people outside the family. There's a nice man who walks his dog, Akis, at around the same time of day as I get my regular outing. I knew he had treats as I could smell them and I initially tried directly accessing his pockets which only succeeded in getting me a sharp telling off from 'Her Indoors'. However, I persisted in looking hungry every time I saw him, until his wife was moved by my woeful face and made him give me a treat. Now every time I see him, I give the command, by sitting down to attention, and he comes up with the goodies.

The other morning however, there was a slight breakdown in our arrangement. I saw Akis as usual and, after a brief hello, went rushing past to find Mr Akis, but he wasn't there. It was Mrs Akis instead and she had forgotten the treats. I still gave her the full treatment: sitting looking hungry, with my paw held up, trembling slightly; just to make the point. Apparently Mr Akis was in hospital having an operation on his hip and expressly told Mrs Akis not to venture out without the treats and I think my name may have been mentioned. What a great chap and what a good response to my training regime, although it was a little disappointing that Mrs Akis had forgotten his instructions. I'm working on getting second helpings but that's advanced training so takes a bit longer.

Another person who's responding well to training is a colleague and friend of 'Her Indoors', Danielle. She occasionally calls round and there's always a lot of laughter when she's about. She stopped for lunch one day so I gave her my best starving dog treatment. The trembling paw touch was a particular winner although it was rather spoilt by 'Her Indoors' listing everything I'd eaten that day. Still, Danielle's not a dog owner and was so completely taken in that 'Her Indoors' gave her a dog biscuit to give to me. I ate it in one gulp of course, and Danielle was so taken aback by my speed of consumption that she gave me a little talking to. Apparently, I should be like a squirrel with his nuts and save some until later! Well catching a squirrel has been an unconsummated ambition of mine for many years, and I don't have any nuts since that little operation when I was about a year old. Still the biscuit was nice.

25TH MARCH – DARK CONFESSIONS
I have a dark, secret prejudice: I don't like postmen. I know this isn't unusual amongst dogs, but I have an ASBO from the post office. One time, when 'Junior Him' was answering the bell at the side gate, I managed to sneak out. Now I'd like to make it clear that I didn't actually harm the Postman, but apparently I had guilty intent. A barking dog whose mind is full of impure thoughts, even an old, small one with blunt teeth, is sufficient. 'Her Indoors' got a letter warning that if there was any repeat of my poor behaviour, we would be blacklisted and they wouldn't deliver post to the

house anymore. The shame. 'Her Indoors' was mortified as ultimately, I'm her responsibility, and I was in big trouble for weeks. I should have been a cat. They can get away with poohing where they want, biting, scratching and killing little creatures and no-one gets a letter. Anyway, since then, strenuous efforts have been made to keep me away from post/delivery people. We've got more warning signs than a nuclear weapons installation, including one in French that 'Him Indoors' bought in Paris, that says 'Attention, chien bizarre!' It amuses 'Him Indoors' no end.

'Her Indoors', rather charitably, in my opinion, wonders if a delivery/post person was unkind to me at some point in the past, but I can't really rationalise it myself; the red mist just descends.

Anyway, I was out on my walk this morning, when we bumped into our local, friendly representative of the Royal Mail. I've heard 'Her Indoors' talking to him before, and aside from his postal disposition, he seems like a nice chap. Ignoring the warnings from 'Her Indoors', he advanced, proffering a biscuit. I was so astonished I ate the biscuit and allowed him to stroke me. Years of prejudice were breached in one fell swoop. I can't make any promises moving forward but I have a feeling the training tables have been turned and that maybe this old dog can learn new tricks – amazing!

30TH MARCH – COMMON GROUND

Now I'm not an expert, although I have been round the block (and up the lane) a few times, but I've come to recognise that relationships work best if there's some common ground. With me and 'Them Indoors' it's the garden. We all like being out there. 'Him Indoors' does manly things with power tools and garden machinery, whilst 'Her Indoors' does what she does best; supervises 'Him Indoors', establishes order, and expresses her creative, nurturing side through tending her plants and growing veg. I, on the other hand, like to help with the pest control, barking at anything furry or feathered. I also like to assist with the watering and ask repeatedly and inexhaustibly for my ball to be thrown. We're all happy. Today the sun shone and we've been busy doing all of the above – bliss. Me and 'Her Indoors' pottered round quite happily, with 'Her' giving me a little commentary on the state of the plants after the winter and occasionally asking my opinion. I just tried to look intelligent.

'Him Indoors' decided to start putting up a new greenhouse and got all the bits out, moaning about a lack of labels and poor instructions that hadn't survived translation from their original Chinese. I tried to help by sitting in the middle of it all, hiding a few key pieces that I wasn't even aware I was sitting on. It all looked pretty complicated to me. The old greenhouse was very tatty although it did have a handy missing bottom pane in the door which allowed me free access whenever I felt like it; a kind of dog flap arrangement. I have a feeling the new one won't have this feature. Still, I'm sure I'll be allowed in as the greenhouse is the territory of 'Her Indoors', or it will be when it's completed.

I managed to find my Frisbee when I was outside today. 'Her Indoors' was tending her plants and 'Him Indoors' was puzzling over the greenhouse parts, so I decided to entertain myself with it. I discovered that when held securely by one edge and shaken vigorously backwards and forwards, it acts like a kind of strimmer which is very useful for dead-heading daffodils, at least it would have been if they had finished flowering. Anyway, 'Her Indoors' wasn't best impressed and after repeated scolding, the Frisbee was removed to the top of the water butt where I couldn't reach it. Charming! Still, I'm wondering whether to patent the idea.

I think I might have lost some of my fitness over the winter. I found all that running around, playing and barking at squirrels, crows, rabbits and anything else that looked worthy of investigation, frankly exhausting. I think 'Her Indoors' has lost a bit of her fitness too. After a few hours in the garden she seemed a bit weary. She'll have to get in training if we're going to get our usual supply of veg and flowers for the house. Still, we've got the whole summer ahead of us so there will be plenty of time for us to build up our strength and for 'Him Indoors' to work out how all the greenhouse parts fit together. After all, the garden is where we're all happy. It's our common ground.

31ST MARCH – EASTER ENTERTAINING

Easter time is not as much fun as it used to be. There was a time when Easter egg hunts with cryptic clues, were the order of the day. 'Junior Him' used to try and find his eggs as quickly as possible and then struggled with the anagram, made up from the letters found with each egg, at the end of the hunt. 'Junior Her' was slower with the finding but quicker with the anagram, so the result was usually close. I just used to join in with the general excitement. Those days have gone unfortunately. 'Junior Him' is still at uni finishing off a project and 'Junior Her' can't really do an Easter egg hunt on her own. I couldn't even eat the eggs if I found them, as chocolate is poisonous to dogs, but, I did get a special, doggy egg myself this year, which is a first, and we had visitors today which was nice. Some things at least are consistent.

chapter Four - April

I found out a few interesting facts about my friends and neighbours recently. Barnie from next door is a Beagle which is a type of scent hound, and apparently Barnie is good at tracking squirrels. He's managed to catch one, which is more than I've ever done, in spite of years of trying. Barnie is a rescue dog but originally comes from Spain. I wonder if he understands Spanish? He understands me alright which is the main thing.

I discovered that Akis, whose owner is generous with treats, is Greek. You'd never guess to look at him. I wonder if he likes yoghurt?

I originally came from Hastings, which isn't that far away, so I'm feeling rather dull by comparison. 'Them Indoors' did take me on holiday once to the borders, where our breed originates from. They've got a photo of me looking cold and miserable on Hadrian's Wall. Border Terriers might hale from those parts, but I'm a softy southerner – what can I tell you.

'Her Indoors' went to the pub recently with a group of friends, one of whom is a French lady who owns a Labrador cross.

35

Apparently, they first had the dog when they lived in France and it was trained to French commands, but now it lives in England it has learnt the English version and responds to both. A bi-lingual dog! 'Her Indoors' was very impressed and has started to speak to me, rather hopefully, in French. I'm bi-lingual too; I ignore her in both languages!

7TH APRIL – DOGGY DILEMMAS

'Him Indoors' decided to take advantage of a break in the showers today and mow the lawn – noisy, smelly and potentially hazardous. The lawn mower's a bit of a problem too! I don't like it, which leaves me with only two possible solutions: one is I go indoors which I hate doing because I like to be out in the garden with my family, and the other is to stick as closely as possible to 'Her Indoors' to allay my nervousness. I'm sure that she feels my physical closeness can only help our bond, but she does occasionally mutter about my dog's breath and the fact that I'm sitting just where she wants to dig with her trowel. If 'Him Indoors' comes too close, she finds my efforts to climb onto her lap a little inhibiting but it's a question of priorities; which is more important, me or the weeds?

The sun came out briefly so I was able to do a little re-familiarisation with the best basking spots in the garden. It changes according to the time of day so I have to deploy myself tactically. One of the best spots is lying next to the end wall of the garden office belonging to 'Her Indoors'. It's south facing and matt black so it absorbs the heat. It's the ideal spot for a Border Terrier to toast his paws I can tell you. It's also a good vantage point to make sure 'Them Indoors' are keeping hard at it. It's quite a large garden so requires a bit of work to keep it nice. I like to lend a bit of moral support when the sunbathing gets a bit too much, by sitting and panting loudly, close to where 'Her Indoors' is busy working. It's the least I can do.

10TH APRIL – THE BUNNIES ARE BACK

I don't know where they go to in the winter, but the bunnies are back. If we get over to the playing field before the other local dogs have had a go, they're there, waiting for me when 'Her Indoors' lets me off the lead. I know it's unlikely that I'll catch one but I always run at them headlong, barking, and watch them scatter – great fun. Then there's the little blighters in the garden. They hide under the shrubs and hedges but I consider it my duty to flush them out. 'Her Indoors' approves – she doesn't like them because they eat her plants. Whilst barking in the garden is not generally tolerated, I've noticed that she turns a deaf ear if I'm chasing the rabbits. Anyway, they've learnt that if they can get through the wire mesh fence to next door, they can flaunt themselves safe in the knowledge that I'm too big to squeeze through. Charlie, the dog next door on the other side to Barnie, has his heart in the right place as far as rabbits are concerned, but he's getting a bit elderly for chasing, bless him.

This evening I got a bit fed up with all the bunnies taunting me, and tried to climb through the fence to teach them a thing or two. The problem was, my collar got caught up and I got stuck. I could hear 'Her Indoors' calling me back in, but I couldn't move. Fortunately, she came looking for me and had a fair idea where I might be so she eventually found me. The trouble is, I was in a particularly inaccessible part of the garden and she's a lot bigger than a Border Terrier. To her credit, she battled through the branches, brambles and stingy nettles, but the language was a bit ripe. I've learnt a few interesting new words to add to my vocabulary but I don't think they're the kind of thing you'd hear on Radio Four. She did manage to unhook me without resorting to wire cutters, but I was sent indoors. I bet the rabbits are laughing right now, but they want to watch their little bunny steps. Revenge is a dish best served cold, and it's cold they'll be if I have anything to do with it. I know where they live.

12TH APRIL – NEWCOMERS

There's a new dog in the village, a Highland Terrier puppy, aged seven months and a junior version of my neighbour of the same breed, Dolly. 'Her Indoors' made such a fuss of it that you'd think she'd never seen a puppy before. Honestly, at her age. I tried being disapproving but 'Her Indoors' just made a hurtful derogatory comment, something I didn't quite catch, but which definitely included the words 'old' and 'grumpy'. These young dogs have no idea about personal space and boundaries, and need setting on the right track from the outset if you ask me. Anyway, my censure didn't work because the owner just scooped the dog up so that 'Her Indoors' could make a proper fuss of it. She even allowed it to chew her knuckles. If I did that kind of thing I'd be in big trouble. I don't understand it, if she wants cute little eyebrows and a tufty moustache she's got me – and 'Him Indoors' of course.

There's also a Shih Tzu that's moved into one of the oast houses. We've met on the playing fields and I must say she seems a friendly sort of dog, in an oriental kind of way. She's not too big and boisterous either which is a plus. She was wearing a smart red coat, although not as smart as mine. She's got the colour wrong too. Red makes you stand out so that your owner can easily keep an eye on you. Green, like mine, helps you fade into the background which can be very useful. Still, as she's a local now, I'll hopefully get a few opportunities to teach her a thing or two. I like to cascade my knowledge where I can.

Some dogs just pass through the village, and I met one the other day who was visiting from Brighton. He's a Greyhound with a very impressive turn of speed. I used to think I was pretty quick when I was younger. I tuck my tail between my legs and sprint. Being pretty short I have an impressive turning circle and can still out-manoeuvre most other dogs which comes in handy occasionally, if I get myself into a little dispute. Anyway, the Greyhound was incredible. He trotted around quite happily until he saw a bunny in the distance and then he effortlessly switched gear and literally flew. It was like being next to a Formula One racing car whilst being in a go-cart. Still, he was a friendly sort of dog and very tall. I could have walked under him, through his legs, without touching his underside, but I didn't like to be too familiar as we'd only just been introduced. It was nice meeting with him and 'Her Indoors' had a good chat to his owner. I hope he passes through the village again sometime.

I got some sad news the other week. An old friend of mine, Carla, has died. She was a Golden Labrador, owned by Ann, one of 'Her Indoors' dog walking friends, and although she had a habit of trying to put me in my place, always a tricky endeavour, she was a nice dog who used to wander round at home carrying a heart-shaped cushion. There's only me and Storm, a Collie cross, left from the original batch of dog walkers' dogs, which is a bit sobering. On Twitter, when a dog passes on it's called 'going over the rainbow bridge' or OTRB, which I think is rather lovely, so I prefer to imagine this is what's happened to Carla.

13TH APRIL – OTHER ANIMALS
One of the advantages with living in the countryside is the variety of other animals that share your space. In addition to the wildlife, there are domestic animals and livestock which I'm not allowed

to bark at. These include sheep, horses, cows and alpacas. The sheep are very tempting because they stare at you through the fence in a confrontational, insolent way. They also scatter very satisfyingly if you bark at them, but this is seriously frowned upon by 'Her Indoors', particularly at this time of year when they've got lambs.

Although I don't get on with Gyp the farm dog, I have to admit he's got a bit of a way with sheep. He can get the whole flock of them moving in the direction that Debbie the Farmer wants them to go in. He can separate them into groups and he doesn't bark. He just slinks around, circling. It's frankly quite exhausting to watch and I have to go home and have a little lie down in my basket, on my cushion, in the warm.

As far as other farm animals are concerned, cows are a bit of a waste of time in my view. They're quite big so I have to watch my step and they don't seem to be bothered by my barking. They just stand there, gazing through the fence at me, emitting methane. Haven't they heard of climate change?

Alpacas on the other hand, are pretty amazing. They've got long necks so they can crane over the hedges, and big eyes and ears. They come in a range of different colours and have impressive eyebrows and splodges in various shades, making their faces characterful and distinctive. They are also rather inquisitive and like to know what's going on in the lane beyond their field. Anyway, when I first met one up close I couldn't quite believe my eyes; I'd never seen an animal like it. I even forgot to bark which is worrying for a terrier. I literally had to be dragged away which led to some good natured teasing from 'Them Indoors' about me wanting one for a pet. Actually, that's not a bad idea. It would be one in the eye for Gyp the farm dog; he's only got sheep.

'Her Indoors' has a bit of a soft spot for our feathered friends. She feeds them during the winter and encourages them to nest on our patch by putting boxes up. I'm not sure I understand it. What do they do for her other than waking her up early at this time of year with their daily racket and eating their way through their own body-weight in peanuts during cold snaps. Occasionally I've managed to sneak a quick sample of the bird food and I must admit I rather like peanuts and stand hopefully watching in case 'Her Indoors' drops any whilst she's filling the container. On one memorable occasion, the 'phone rang and she absent-mindedly left the bag of peanuts on the floor. By the time she got back I'd eaten my way through approximately half of them. She was not impressed and my poohs looked like a well-known peanut confectionary bar for days.

I made the mistake once of confusing a bag containing Niger seeds with the peanut bag (the same plastic bag from the pet shop – an easy error to make) and when I saw an opportune moment I dashed in for a quick snack. Unfortunately I knocked the bag over and the seed went everywhere which didn't please 'Her Indoors'. They were not very tasty either and they got stuck in between my teeth. Still, 'Her Indoors' has got some dried meal worms that the Robin seems to like so I'm trying for those next time. I bet they're crunchy and taste like chicken.

Anyway, nesting is always a bit of a dodgy time for me. There was that unfortunate incident when 'Her Indoors' had been watching a pair of blackbirds who had nested close to the landing window. She had followed them through the nest building stage, laying eggs, hatching, with her worrying about natural predators such as squirrels and magpies. Once they'd fledged however, one youngster happened to flutter out right under my paws. What was

I supposed to do? 'Her Indoors' yelled at me so sharply, it put me off my stride and no real harm was done, but she was still cross.

Then there was my tragic encounter with a baby Blue Tit, that didn't end quite so well. Even 'Junior Her' was cross with me that time, although I think the term 'Blue Tit Murderer' was a bit strong. There was no intention to harm, I just moved in close for a better look. I think it must have died of shock.

The worst was the business with the Mallards last year. I was in the garden at the weekend, snuffling about in the back border, next to the house (there's a reason why we're called Border Terriers), when I discovered a duck. It was a bit of a surprise to be frank. We're not even near any water. She left it a bit late to shift as well, so there was an exciting moment when I chased her down the garden before she cheated and took off, leaving me barking in her wake. I got told off by 'Him Indoors'. Anyway, I returned to the back border to see if there were any more ducks lurking, and discovered a nest full of eggs. When 'Him Indoors' found I'd chased her off her nest he was even more cross with me. 'Her Indoors' did point out, rather lamely in my opinion, that it wasn't my fault, but 'Him Indoors' was rather put out about the whole thing, particularly when the duck didn't return to her nest. The 'murderer' term was bandied about again which wasn't fair; the eggs hadn't even hatched. At what point does an egg become a duck? 'Junior Him' stuck up for me on the 'phone and pointed out that I couldn't be a murderer as I didn't have 'guilty intent' – I knew that A-level in law would come in handy at some point – so 'Her Indoors' suggested an alternative plea of manslaughter on the grounds of diminished responsibility due to a terrier disposition. I didn't know such a defence existed, but what do I know, I'm just a dog.

Still, the event wasn't over. The next morning, just as the whole episode was slipping quietly into my rather considerable back catalogue of misdemeanours, I made the mistake of double checking the back border just in case, and found she'd returned over night. It was like being stuck in a repeating performance loop. On this occasion however, the duck returned a short time later and, after much hesitation, returned to her nest. I was only allowed in the back garden on my lead and under close supervision for weeks after that. Mallard eggs take a long time to hatch.

Anyway, today there was a little mishap that wasn't my fault. 'Her Indoors' was busy moving stuff into her new greenhouse, which 'Him Indoors' has finally finished, when she went to shift a half used bag of compost which was on top of a garden chair round the back of the garage. She opened it up to check on its state and discovered a Robin's nest complete with four eggs. I don't know who was more surprised, 'Her Indoors' or the incubating mother. The Robin appears to have returned to the nest and 'Her Indoors' has bought another bag of compost, so no harm done. It's just as well I wasn't close by otherwise I'm sure it would have been my fault. I notice I've been banned from going round the back of the garage now though. Honestly......

28TH APRIL – NEAR MISS

I'm in trouble again and it's not my fault. The good news is that the Robin chicks fledged this morning. The bad news is that I discovered this interesting fact when a baby Robin flew out from under my paws. I was just about to give the little miscreant the instinctive terrier response when 'Her Indoors' shouted at me with a 'you do that and I'll make a hearth rug out of you' type of voice that I instantly recognised from the blackbird incident. Next thing I know, I'm whisked indoors, and exercised for the rest of the day on the lead – again.

I don't understand why baby birds leave the nest before they can fly properly. This baby Robin, undaunted by his near death experience, zig-zagged and swooped round the garden, just clear of the ground, crash landing at frequent intervals like an inebriated pilot. What is a self-respecting terrier supposed to do? Still, at least my vigilance means that cats are a rare sighting. It's amazing any baby birds survive to adulthood. All we need now is another ducks' nest and it'll be like Groundhog Day. Perhaps I better check the back border just in case, although I'd better not let anyone see me. We dogs are not supposed to be able to remember things over long periods of time like a year, and I don't want to shatter anyone's illusions.

30TH APRIL - SNACK ATTACK

'Them Indoors' had beef stew for tea. Bliss! 'Her Indoors' isn't very generous in the snacking department. In fairness, it's her who has to answer to the Vet at my annual check-up if I've gained during the year, so she tends to be rather cautious. She does however have a pleasing weakness for giving me the left over gravy from a stew. Delicious. I know as soon as she starts cooking it, and as it takes a long time, there's hours of anticipation. The worst bit is after she's served the rest of the family, waiting for it to cool. I can barely contain myself. When the moment finally arrives, I pretty much lick the pattern off my bowl in an effort not to waste any. It might seem an extreme reaction, but you try living on tinned dog meat and a handful of dry mixer.

chapter Five - May

It's been a lovely warm weekend, finally, and I'm pleased to announce the first barbeque of the season has taken place. I went through all the usual anxieties as to whether they'd remember my divine right to the last sausage, but fortunately 'Them Indoors' hadn't forgotten, and my begging demeanour together with my pathetic whimpering, helped to secure that final goal. I always have to wait for it to cool down. I'm used to eating my meat cold, often straight out of a tin in the fridge, so without going into sordid details, my digestion can't cope with anything too hot and 'Them Indoors' have learnt, through bitter experience, to give my offerings sufficient cooling time.

I have to be careful not to over-play my hand at barbeque events. If I'm too much of a nuisance they send me indoors. Sometimes it's worth it, for example if they leave bowls of crisps lying around. They really should know better. Then there are unintended spillages of food and occasionally beer. I probably shouldn't confess it, but I'm rather partial to the odd drop of the amber nectar. Ice cream is nice too, although it's a bit cold on the teeth.

Occasionally I've got into serious trouble during outdoor meal times. The barbeque itself lives in the shed in the garden, which is the territory of 'Him Indoors' and therefore out of bounds to anything remotely canine. One time however, he forgot to shut the shed door and he'd left a packet of organic garden fertilizer standing on the shed floor. It was very tasty. After a major panic in case I'd poisoned myself, 'Them Indoors' discovered it was in fact pelleted chicken manure and was unlikely to cause me any real harm. 'Him Indoors' just indulged in some unseemly name calling that involved the words 'disgusting' and 'dog' in close proximity to each other. Unfortunately, it did have a rather adverse effect on my digestion, right in the middle of their main course, which started 'Him Indoors' off again on how he'd never wanted a dog in the first place – honestly, I'm ten years old – fancy bringing that up..

Anyway, talking of bringing things up, 'Him Indoors' thought he'd out-manoeuvre me by using the fertilizer for its intended purpose, and sprinkling it around the plants. As he doesn't trust me, he decided to bury it, just to be on the safe side. Nothing daunted, I had a happy time, when 'Them Indoors' were distracted, digging it all up and eating it anyway. That'll teach them to go organic; I wouldn't touch that chemical stuff with a barge-pole – I have my standards.

Fortunately however, today's barbeque was without incident and I finally got what I'd been waiting for. Waitrose: venison and pork if I'm not much mistaken. I'm something of a connoisseur. Roll on summer!

I've seen a few old friends on walks recently. Bouncing Betty was on good form, living up to her name by the fence. Her jumping just has to be seen to be believed. I wish I could do it. I'd put the skill to much better use than just bouncing up and down along her boundary. Maybe I need to have a word with her.

I also saw the smallest dog in the village too the other day. Although he's tiny, he's a very friendly and confident little chap. I heard somewhere that Pomeranians were two of only three dogs that survived the sinking of the Titanic. It probably helped that they were so small they didn't take up any space in the life rafts. Anyway, he's a plucky little chap and he doesn't seem daunted by other dogs, even though we're a lot bigger, but his owner seems pretty careful. I can't say I blame her. If it's anything like me and 'Her Indoors', she will be the reliable source of rescue should a touch of small dog assertiveness create any problems of a physical nature with other canines.

There's a new dog moved in down one of the lanes. He's a big chap – a long haired German Shepherd. I gave him the usual brisk terrier introduction with 'Her Indoors' muttering under her breath that if I upset this one, I was on my own. I don't know what she means. Anyway, the dog just cowered against the fence looking scared and miserable. His owner explained to 'Her Indoors' that small dogs keep picking on him so he's got a bit of a complex. I tried to be sympathetic but he really needs to pull himself together. I might be a bit vocal, but I wouldn't do any harm.

Talking of doing harm, I saw 'that Red Setter from up the road' and we both had a bracing exchange of views. 'Her Indoors' got chatting to the owner when she bumped into them without me the other day, making conversation possible for once. Apparently the dog's name is Todd. I can't say I care much what he's called. He'll always be 'that Red Setter from up the road' to me.

12TH MAY – DOGS-IN-LAW

In addition to my friends and foes in the village, I have a few dogs-in-law that I get along with. Ollie and Archie are two Labradors belonging to the younger brother of 'Him Indoors'. They live quite locally so I get to walk with them from time to time. They need reminding who's boss, but once we've re-established that, we get along fine. They're generally quite trusting so they can be lead into trouble easily; a good quality in a dog.

They used to have a house with a river running through the garden which was lovely to look at but which had a lot of smelly mud in the shallows. Anyway, being a gundog breed, they liked to go into the water and were constantly having to be hosed down. As a consequence of this, they were banned from the river. Now I don't like water; I'm a terrier, which I believe comes from the Latin 'terra' meaning 'of the earth', with no mention of the wet stuff. 'Him Indoors' believes the word terrier is derived from 'terrorist' but he's prejudiced so I'm sticking with my version. Anyway, my dislike of water didn't stop me from encouraging Ollie and Archie in their leisure pursuits. I ran with them companionably, right up to the water's edge, and then stopped in my tracks whilst they went in. They got told off sharply and were unsympathetically hosed down with cold water whilst I watched, looking all innocent, which is a difficult expression for me to convincingly muster. That'll teach them to misbehave.

Still, they got their own back when I was over there recently. We were all enjoying our own chews, when the doorbell rang. I immediately sounded the alarm and disappeared off to investigate. When I got back, my chew had mysteriously vanished. I wondered why neither of them had barked at the door bell. If they hadn't both been in the room with me at the time, I would have suspected one of them of ringing it. They could reach if they stood on their back paws. They're supposed to be family – honestly!

Another dog-in-law, but one I haven't met yet, is Midge. She belongs to the sister of 'Her Indoors' and is a Poodle - Cocker Spaniel cross. I've been sent a photo of her reading my blog so she's obviously an intelligent creature. I think we're going to get along just fine.

We've recently had an edition to the wider family, in the form of Alice, who's a Jack Russell puppy. She belongs to the brother of 'Her Indoors' – they're clearly all a dog owning kind of family. Anyway, another terrier in the family is the cause of particular satisfaction, so I wrote her a letter welcoming her and passing on my good advice, as follows:

Dear Alice,

I thought I'd extend a personal welcome to my newest dog-in-law, particularly as you're the only other terrier in the extended family. You join a venerable group of canines I can tell you. The wider family are all dog lovers, and I can tell, from the puppy pictures on Facebook, that your family are completely besotted. Although you are only eight weeks old, you've made a wise first move by picking the right home to grace with your presence.

Now I've got a few miles on the clock so I thought I'd share a bit of my acquired wisdom and help you to cut a few corners.

Firstly, you need to quickly establish who's boss. There's likely to be a family pecking order and you need to ensure your correct position in it.

You also need to make sure you don't catch on too quickly in the training department. I know we dogs are naturally eager to please, but you should curb that amiable instinct in order to extract the maximum rewards for each new skill mastered. When we first moved to the country, I used to bark at horses. 'Her Indoors' bribed me copiously with treats, and I eventually succumbed, but if she forgets more than once to reward my compliance, I make sure I promptly relapse.

Ensure you choose your own friends and don't allow them to foist any old pooch on you. After all, they choose theirs. Whatever you do, don't adopt a consistent rationale for who you like and who you don't. It keeps your family on their toes. They also take an instant dislike to individuals occasionally, so reserve the right to do likewise. In your interactions with other canines, bear in mind that you may be small, but you are all dog, and don't allow yourself to be bossed around. I don't.

Remember that you are not a person and don't allow them to treat you as one. See the world through your own eyes and endeavour to get your family to consider your particular canine viewpoint and disposition.

Your job description is 'family pet' and, although you're a rural dog like me, and probably have a terrier's instinct when it comes to rabbits and other undesirables, don't allow your family to exploit the 'any other duties' clause. All rabbit chasing I do is clearly on my own terms and I completely resist any attempts to get me out of bed early or in bad weather in order to fulfil this function. I suggest you do likewise.

Which leads to my next point: make sure you safeguard your own creature comforts. Identify, at the earliest possible stage, where the best places are to sleep, warm up, cool down or loiter for potential treats, whether accidental or deliberate.

Take your responsibilities to your junior family very seriously. Role play is an important business and you can be a monster, an alien, a princess or a noble steed with very little adaptation. Love them unconditionally, and they will return it in heaps. You have a duty to prepare the next generation of dog-lovers. My juniors, although grown-up now, have already planned what dogs they will own in the future: a whippet and a Dachshund respectively. Whilst I'm a bit disappointed that Border Terriers don't feature, these are worthy breeds and I've clearly brought them up with decent values. Treasure your playtimes; children grow up very quickly.

However, beware of dressing up clothes, water pistols and sledges.

Live life in the moment and look for the opportunity to extract every possible bit of fun and enjoyment from any given situation. Dogs and people are meant to be together and we make worthy companions on the journey through life. Jack Russell's are a plucky breed so live up to your heritage.

And finally, don't let them realise how much you really understand. It's best to hide your intellectual light under a bushel. Always take any opportunity to learn new skills. My 'Junior Her' taught me how to read as a puppy. Word processing was a natural development from that and it's stood me in good stead, as you can see.

That's it for now. I know we live on opposite sides of the country but I hope we get to meet soon. I usually get on okay with other terriers and I've got a few tricks of the trade which would be best to teach you in person.

Warmest regards
Rolo

15TH MAY – FUN AND FROLICS

I once heard that some dogs who end up homeless and in rescue centres, have never learnt how to play and don't know what to do with a toy when they're given one, which is very sad. I thankfully, don't suffer from that problem, and have received a steady supply of toys ever since I was a puppy. In fact one memorable Christmas I actually got more presents than 'Her Indoors' which didn't go down too well.

One of my favourite games is to get 'Her Indoors' to chase me around the breakfast bar in the kitchen, and pretend she wants to get my rubber ball off me. I bounce around, doing play-bows and mock growling. 'Her Indoors' gets into the spirit of things, on all fours, growling back. She's no idea what she's saying, bless her, and some of that language definitely didn't come from me, but she gives it her best efforts.

It's not without its hazards though. One time 'Her Indoors' was under the breakfast bar, forgot where she was, and stood up, cracking her head. She was okay but the language was pretty colourful. It's just as well she didn't knock herself out; she would have had fun trying to explain that one in Casualty. On occasions, the stools under the breakfast bar are left too close to the wall and I can't get through. 'Her Indoors' usually moves them to allow me safe passage, but I have been known to get stuck trying to squeeze through. This morning, I tried going under the horizontal supports on the stool but there wasn't sufficient space and I almost had the stool over. Worse still, I let go of the ball and 'Her Indoors' got it, which isn't allowed, under my rules. I had to bark until she relented and gave it back. I'm not a good loser. Generally, when I get tired or there's any danger of 'Her Indoors' getting the ball, I retreat to my bed and lie on it. That sorts things!

18TH MAY – LURKING DANGERS

Now I certainly don't consider myself a timid dog, but there are one or two things in the house that I have a fear of, which seems to amuse 'Them Indoors'. For example, you can't trust a carrier bag. They might be lying there, all innocently scrunched up and still, when without provocation, they start to unfurl, which is most unnerving. The correct response, clearly, is to bark at them.

Similarly, I have a fear of the tray cupboard in the kitchen. 'Her Indoors' uses it to store not only trays, but spare kitchen roll, spaghetti in a tin, and cartons of fruit juice. Occasionally, she over-stacks, and as it is at floor level and there is only a curtain across it rather than a door, the contents fall out on top of me, when I'm innocently minding my own business in my bed. 'Her Indoors' is always apologetic when this happens, but she's made me so nervous that when she goes in there to retrieve something, I hastily vacate my bed just in case. I have to say that 'Them Indoors' both shamelessly exploit this situation. If they want me to get out of my bed but I'm refusing to budge, for example on a cold winter's night when I'm all cosy and sleepy and they want me to go into the garden to do my nightly ablutions, they go into the tray cupboard and rattle the trays so that I shoot out. This is a low and underhand tactic that is frankly beneath them. They won't be laughing when they get my therapy bill.

Another fear based on an unfortunate experience, is that of bunches of flowers. This goes back a long time, when we lived in our previous house and I used to sleep in the utility room. 'Her Indoors' received a bouquet of flowers, cellophane wrapped, and placed them in a plastic jug on the worktop. Unfortunately, they toppled over, and landed on my head, as I was snoozing. I've never forgotten and treat all subsequent bunches of flowers with the suspicion they deserve.

I also don't like any sign of packing; it makes me nervous as it usually means someone is deserting me. It's not too bad if it's just one person, but occasionally the whole family abandons me for a holiday. They always make careful arrangements to ensure my well-being, but it's just not the same thing as being in your own home with your own people. Anyway, I don't know how they can enjoy themselves when I'm not with them. The other packing experience that rather haunts me is the time they moved house when I wasn't looking. After weeks of shoving things into boxes, they packed me off into doggy day-care, and when I came home again, I discovered it wasn't where I'd left it. It took me months to readjust.

23RD MAY – EURO AVERSION

I watched the Eurovision Song Contest last night with 'Them Indoors' but I'm beginning to wonder if, like your politics, this is something you should keep to yourself. I thought it was entirely normal for the family to gather round the television and to listen to hours of dubious music, glitzy staging and frankly worrying dancing, scoring each song carefully out of ten, and voting for the one that gets the most marks from our discerning panel of 'Them Indoors'. However, when I innocently posted a picture on Twitter of me watching the TV, the response was varied to say the least. I'm sure that an alternative suggestion of poking your eyeballs out with toothpicks, would be less fun, and I have to say in our defence that me and 'Her Indoors' dozed comfortably through a good part of it and then went to bed before the scoring, but 'Him Indoors' stayed up. Should I be worried about him? I'm not sure if I should tell but he was even playing the winning song in the study this morning. Perhaps it's his age? Anyway, I'm wondering whether to get a group of Border Terriers together for next year. I used to howl when 'Junior Her' played her violin so I've obviously got some musical sensibilities. There must be millions of dog lovers across Europe and I'm sure they'd all vote for us. I bet we'd do better than fourth from bottom anyway. Watch this space......

'Her Indoors' is a keen gardener and I like to help out where I can. In the summer, she does the watering in the evening, after tea and this is my favourite part of the day. I trot round with her as she examines her plants, and assist with the watering. I like to think that I've made a contribution to the distinctive flavour of the home grown produce. The veg plot is also a good area for self-service. One year, 'Her Indoors' decided to grow those little alpine strawberries – delicious! 'Her Indoors' thought it was the birds that were stealing the fruit until she caught me el flagrante, with my head in the patch. I blame 'Junior Her'. She taught me how to pick my own blackberries many years ago and it's a lesson I've not forgotten.

Then there was that unfortunate business with the slug traps one year. It had been a wet spring and the little blighters had been munching their way through the vulnerable young veg plants and 'Her Indoors' was getting a bit fed up with it. She doesn't really like using chemicals in the garden, so she bought some slug traps which she buried until level with the ground and then filled them with value larger. Apparently, the slugs and snails find the smell of beer irresistible but when drawn to the traps, they fall in and drown. Still, at least they die happy. Anyway, the day after the slug traps were installed, I was a bit under the weather. I didn't want to get out of my bed and was obviously groggy. 'Her Indoors' couldn't understand it as I'd been fine the day before, until she went down to the veg plot and found that someone or something had dug up the slug traps and drunk all of the lager. I'm not sure what the recommended units are for small dogs but I think I had probably exceeded them. Still, a few slugs had been killed before I got to the beer, and these were quite tasty when sufficiently marinated. 'Her Indoors' redid the slug traps, but covered them with heavy terracotta pots raised slightly off the ground to let the slugs in but keep small dogs out. Spoil sport.

This year 'Her Indoors' got 'Him Indoors' to fence the veg plot in with some chicken wire. This was supposedly to keep the rabbits out but I have my doubts. I am occasionally let in when 'Her Indoors' is weeding, but only under direct supervision which is a pity. Gardening is one of my favourite pastimes and I like to display my creativity and oneness with nature.

chapter Six – June

I had my annual outing to the Vet's a couple of weeks ago, for a check up and some vaccinations. I must say, I quite enjoy it. There are all those interesting basket cases to investigate: a parrot and a black cat on this occasion. There are also other dogs, and a range of rare and exciting smells. Then there's the Vets themselves: a pleasant young lady this time around. She spoke to me nicely, admiring my youthful sprightliness, and examined me all over for lumps and bumps which I rather like – any attention is better than no attention. She did the usual things like listening to my heart and checking my teeth which were all fine apparently.

'Her Indoors' gets a bit stressed as my behaviour tends to deteriorate with all the excitement. She still hasn't forgotten the encounter with the Macaw from the local zoo that time, or the unfortunate incident with the bunny in a box. She lets me chase them in the garden – inconsistent boundaries I call it. Anyway, I know there's usually a biscuit coming so I treat everything the Vet proffers as a possible food source: rubber gloves, stethoscope, syringe, you

57

name it. One time the Vet forgot to reward my compliance and I had to stage a sit-down protest until the biscuit was hastily offered. It's part of the deal.

The dodgy moment however, is when I have to go on the scales. One year I'd overdone it on the treat front and the Vet was rather stern. 'Her Indoors' immediately put me on a diet, and to make matters worse, nagged the other members of the family into not giving me any little snacks. It was dreadful. Anyway, this year I'd lost a little bit of weight so the Vet gave me two biscuits as a reward. I like her style!

We had to go back for a second visit today, as they couldn't do all my vaccinations in one go; apparently it's a bit too much for my immune system. This time we got a new, young, very enthusiastic Vet. She was so diligent she was running half an hour late, which is unusual as they're normally very punctual. Anyway, thirty minutes of keeping me distracted made 'Her Indoors' a bit tense and when we finally went in, we got a repeat of my previous visit. The Vet checked my heart; it was still there. She checked my teeth and pointed out to 'Her Indoors' my build up of plaque. 'Her Indoors' felt obliged to mention, in my defence, that the previous Vet had said that my teeth were generally okay for a dog of my age. She then wanted to weight me, but 'Her Indoors' pointed out that I was unlikely to have varied much in two weeks. There was a lengthy Veterinary monologue about my joints, and although 'Her Indoors' agreed to buy some fish oil tablets, I suspect she only did so to facilitate an escape. She poured a large glass of wine when she got home. She's not supposed to have that on a week day. Her dinner was cold too and she was a bit grumpy when 'Him Indoors' enquired after how much it all cost. Still, they know I'm worth it.

I'm a closet Radio Four listener. I know dogs are only supposed to have a limited vocabulary of words they actually understand, but I've picked up a lot about the outside world from listening to the radio, and not all of it has been good. This week there was an elderly man reportedly savaged to death in his back garden by a neighbour's dog. Honestly, it makes you wonder. Is it due to an innately evil disposition or is it the environment in which they've been brought up and the influences they've been subject to? I suspect it's probably a complicated blend of all of those things, but what do I know, I'm only a small dog of limited understanding.

Still, there was a heart warming story on the local news last night that put everything back into perspective. A young Border Terrier called Lola was being walked by her owner along the cliff tops near Eastbourne, when she chased a bird (surely not, a Border Terrier chasing a bird, whatever was she thinking of...) and was so engrossed in the pursuit that she ran headlong over the edge of the cliff. Although certain that the dog couldn't have survived such a fall, her owner called the local coastguard and, rather miraculously, Lola was rescued safe and well having fallen into the sea and scrambled to safety.

There was a lovely image of a coast guard wading out of the waves, holding Lola tightly to his chest. Then there were the interviews with Lola's family, including a young boy and girl who were clearly thrilled to have Lola safely returned and she was clearly delighted with all the fuss. If you're reading Lola, I know you're only seven months old, but remember to look before you leap next time. Call me a sentimental old dog, but also remember that dogs and people are mean to be happy together and that in spite of everything you see and hear in the media, there is still a lot of good in the world.

Right, I'm off to chase a few birds myself before catching the latest bulletin on the radio.

I've always had a bit of a fascination with cars. Being a rural dog, I don't get to travel in them very often and when I do, it's usually in 'Junior Him's car on the basis that a bit of extra contamination won't be noticed. I always like to have a good root around. I'm not sure where McDonalds is, but I'm convinced I'd like it if I went there.

If I travel with the family in 'Him Indoors' car, I have to go in a pet carrier as he doesn't like me on his leather seats. I'm normally quite well behaved up until the point that I think we've arrived, and I then I start yowling and barking with excitement, which doesn't go down well with the other occupants. Often I mistake the car slowing down or stopping, for the end of the journey, and mis-time my vocals, which, if anything, goes down even worse. Still, at least I'm not travel sick like I was when I was a puppy. On one notable occasion, we'd been to visit the mother of 'Him Indoors' and I'd been digging in her garden. I'd found some daffodil bulbs and gave them the usual terrier treatment – eat first; ask questions later. Unfortunately daffodil bulbs aren't edible, but by the time this factor had registered with my digestion, we were half way home in the car. I was very sick. The only upside was that 'Him Indoors' wasn't with us on that occasion.

I also find the interiors of other people's cars fascinating and have been known to climb into total strangers' given half the chance. The most notable occasion was when the local police were doing a speed trap on the main road. As we went out for our morning constitutional, they were just putting their equipment back in the car, which was parked in the village hall car park. As I was off the lead, I went up to say hello. 'Her Indoors' was slightly concerned that in their reflective jackets I might mistake them for the Postman, but I'm not stupid. Anyway, after a friendly greeting, I climbed into their car and started ferreting about under the seats. The Policemen were a bit surprised. I don't suppose they often get small, furry animals in the back. 'Her Indoors' had to haul me out, apologising and muttering something about me wanting to be a police dog. Still, there were some interesting smells in the back of the car and I felt quite light-headed for some time after...

11TH JUNE – EMBARRASSING MOMENTS

Me and 'Her Indoors' both succeeded in the embarrassment stakes this morning.

When she was walking me over the playing field, there was a man with his dog who we've seen a few times before. The dog meets with my approval because he's calm and friendly. I'm not sure of the breed but I expect there's a bit of poodle in there somewhere as there's a touch of fuzz about his fur. 'Her Indoors' usually exchanges a few pleasantries, about the weather with the owner, so this morning, I thought it was only polite for me to go up and say hello. I did a bit of friendly sniffing and realised, very quickly, that there were some treats in his pocket. I tried asking nicely, sitting down to attention and looking hungry, but that didn't work, so then I tried the direct tactic of starting to follow him home. I have to say that if he was a bit bemused to find a small, bouncing terrier at his side, he hid it pretty well, but 'Her Indoors' was rather embarrassed and kept apologising profusely whilst practising a few of my alternative names, once we were out of ear-shot.

On the way home however, it was the turn of 'Her Indoors' to show herself up. She spotted something in the road, beyond our house, that had been hit by a car. The traffic was slowing down to avoid it, and when she next spotted it, it had moved to the side of the road. Fearing that the last thing an injured creature needed was a Border Terrier bearing down on it, and full of concern, she dropped me off at home and then went on a solo rescue mission.

Unfortunately, the bin liner in question is not expected to recover! Still, her heart is in the right place, bless her, although maybe the middle-aged need for the acquisition of spectacles has come upon her rather sooner than she anticipated.

17TH JUNE – RABBIT'S REVENGE

I've been in trouble again and it's not my fault. I blame the bunnies. Firstly, they cause problems by eating the plants and flaunting themselves, tempting me to bark and chase them. Then, having escaped the jaws of doom, they get sick and die of their own accord. 'Her Indoors' has been doing her best to check the garden before she lets me out, but I was caught in the act of indulging in some bunny snacking so she wasn't best pleased. I don't know why; they put rabbit in dog food for goodness sake, so it's sheer hypocrisy. Anyway, for the sake of family harmony, she omitted to tell 'Him Indoors' about the little incident in the garden. Unfortunately, all that raw meat upset my digestion overnight, and I had a bad case of bunny scented flatulence. 'Him Indoors' complained about the dreadful smell in the kitchen and 'Her Indoors' acted all innocent, checking the bins and drains, when she knew it was me all along. She then had to sneak me some extra charcoal dog biscuits when 'Him Indoors' was at work, to help ease my problem. Still, I was soon back to normal, but the downside is I'm on the lead in the back garden. As I said, it's not my fault.

24TH JUNE – SPORTING TERRIERS

One of the nice things about the summer is the plethora of sporting events. Now I'm an outdoors sort of dog, and as many of these events consist of people chasing after balls in some shape or form, I'm totally in favour of it. Wimbledon has started, which should mean an instant deterioration in the weather. Now it's not that I'm biased, but I'm a big supporter of Andy Murray. He's not only British (have you noticed that Scottish people are only British when they win, otherwise they're Scottish?) it's the fact that he owns not one, but two Border Terriers.

He's obviously a man of some discernment and taste. He gets my vote anyway, which I'm sure is a big comfort to him.

In addition to the tennis, there's often athletics of some sort to enjoy on the TV. The Olympics are good when they're on, but I think all of these events are missing a few sports. There's no 'one hundred metre sprint after a rubber ball' – I could win that. They could also do with a 'squeezing through a tiny hole in the fence, relative to body size', event. Additionally, there's potential for a 'dog carrying the biggest stick' event with additional points for the number of people caught in the back of the knees, and Bouncing Betty would be an obvious contender for the high jump. Medals would have to be edible of course. Anyway, in anticipation, I'd like to thank my coach, 'Her Indoors' for a life time of training ignored. I'd also like to thank 'Him Indoors' and 'Junior Him' for my dietary supplements and 'Junior Her' for supervising my kit and for her unwavering support in moments of crisis. I couldn't have done it without them.

28TH JUNE – GARDEN PERILS

I don't know why, but we've got a plague of flies at the moment. I keep snapping at them but I'm not very accurate – I think my eyesight must be going – so I bark at them, just to release my pent up frustrations and show them who's boss. It's driving 'Them Indoors' mad. 'Her Indoors' sat down and explained to me, in a patient voice, that there was no point barking at them as it wouldn't do any good. It was kind of her to clarify this but doesn't she know that we dogs only have a limited vocabulary of words that we understand, so clearly I couldn't comprehend anything that she was saying.

Sometimes I snap at wasps and bees. The latter in particular, are easier to catch because they are quite big. The only disadvantage is that they sting, but I don't let that stop me. It's like toads. Every spring they come out of hibernation and start crawling and hopping around the garden. I know they don't taste very good as they exude an unpleasant fluid from their skin when they're upset, but I still pick one up every year, just to make sure nothing has changed.

The other animal with a tendency to fight back, in the garden, are the grass snakes. They are attracted to the compost heap due to the warmth generated by all that rotting vegetation. The first time I caught one, I was in the garden with 'Her Indoors' who was happily weeding, and looked up to see me carrying a large, writhing snake. She was most alarmed and shouted at me to drop it. As it was bigger and more wriggly than I'd anticipated, I did let it go momentarily, but nothing daunted, went in for a second try. 'Her Indoors' was shouting and waving her garden trowel around, but the snake had its own defence mechanism and squirted me with a foul smelling liquid right in my face. 'Her Indoors' hauled me indoors and shut me in the kitchen, then went back to the snake which was lying very still with its tongue lolling out. Diagnosing 'death by terrier' and knowing I'd go straight back to the snake once I was let outside, she gingerly picked it up, draped across her hand trowel, and carried it under the hedge.

When she came back into the house, I was still rubbing at my face, so she consulted her Readers Digest book of British Reptiles and confirmed that the liquid they squirt is an irritant, but otherwise harmless. However, what caught her eye was a passage that explained, how grass snakes, when in danger, will often 'play dead' to facilitate an escape. There was a photo of a snake, doing just that, lying very still with its tongue lolling out. Horrified to discover that the snake she had draped over her small trowel, very close to her person, might well have still been alive, she rushed into the garden and looked under the hedge. Sure enough, the snake had gone. How could that have been my fault? Anyway, I didn't get much sympathy over the irritating, foul smelling, liquid, in fact she barely spoke to me for the rest of the day. Charming!

25TH JUNE – BIRTHDAY BLESSINGS

Today is the birthday of 'Him Indoors' and, breaking with tradition
I decided to get him a little present that sums up the nature of our
relationship and mutual regard. I got him a sign that reads 'Never
mind the dog, beware of the owner'. That'll teach him for buying
me the rude French sign 'Attention, Chien Bizzare!'. Anyway,
'Him Indoors' seemed touched by the gesture and said he'd hang
it on his study door. We love each other really...

30TH JUNE - HOT DOGS

Summer has finally arrived and, after less than two weeks of hot
weather, the nation is grumbling and the TV news is starting to show
shots of cracked reservoir beds. There's no pleasing the British public.
There are however some up-sides. 'Her Indoors' usually takes me for a
walk pretty early, before she goes to work, and in the hot weather we've
been joined by quite a few dogs who are normally taken out later, trying
to avoid the heat. I've met the Shih Tzu who I've not seen for a long
time, and we had a pleasurable little frolic. Less enjoyably, I saw that
Red Setter from up the road, at a distance, but he looked a bit subdued.
I should think he's a bit hot with all those long, flowing red locks. I
didn't get close enough to tell him personally, but that serves him right
for being such a pretty boy.

I've spent a lot of time in the garden alternating between sun and
shade. I lie in the sun until it becomes unbearable, then I retreat into the
shade. Occasionally I have to go indoors for a rest on the cold floor tiles
and a drink from my bowl, but I only do that as a last resort. The patio
paving slabs and a quick refreshing drink from the bird bath usually set
me right. The water from the bird bath has more of a distinctive taste
than the clean stuff in the kitchen, so I try and drink there whenever
possible, much to the displeasure of 'Her Indoors' who worries about
the effect on my digestion.

I think I've coped pretty well with the heat. Okay, so I've only got short fur, but there's a soft under layer beneath a rough working exterior so it's two coats in effect. 'Her Indoors' attempted to ease the situation by giving me a good brushing, which made me look like a potential Crufts contender, although it did help a bit.

I go outside last thing at night, for my ablutions, and I usually indulge in some regular back scratching on the rough concrete path outside the back door. Anyway, it was so pleasant, with the cool night air wafting around my under-carriage, that I just lay there, on my back with my paws in the air, contemplating the night sky. 'Her Indoors' was a bit concerned initially, but when she saw it wasn't rigour mortis and I was still breathing, she tried to coax me inside. Nothing doing. She must have been hot too, because she ended up sitting next to me and we spent a pleasant ten minutes cooling off together. Unfortunately, 'Her Indoors' is a bit prone to insect bites and she paid a heavy price. She's looking frankly rather blotchy and doing a lot of moaning. Perhaps she should try dabbing some of my anti-flea stuff on the back of her neck and between her shoulder blades; it works for me.

Anyway, there was a cracking thunder storm last night. 'Them Indoors' had anticipated it and put my bed out in the lobby. I like to think it was out of concern for my well-being, but I suspect it's because they can't hear me so much when I'm out there. I can't really distinguish thunder storms from fireworks; they're all bright flashes and loud bangs, so I treat them both the same and bark loudly, just in case. This morning the air felt a lot fresher and there was a lovely rainbow that stretched across the entire landscape. It looked like it ended down at the farm, but I suspect it'd be no good searching for a pot of gold; all you'd find there is Gyp the farm dog.

chapter Seven - July

3RD JULY – GENIUS DOGS

Now I consider myself pretty smart. I can think my way round most things, including the frankly sometimes petty restrictions that 'Them Indoors' place on my actions. In fact I try most of the time not to let on how smart I am as I've learnt it's wise to keep your cards pretty close to your chest.

'Them Indoors' have been watching a series of programmes on the TV about the intelligence of dogs during which they put various breeds through their paces. One test included putting a blanket loosely over the unsuspecting canine's head and seeing how long it took them to remove it. I should have guessed what was coming next – the BBC should be a bit more responsible. Before I could say 'remote control' I had a blanket put over my head. It took me about three seconds which is just behind the Border Collie on the program. It's not that I'm a bad loser, it's just that I'm a small dog and it was rather a big blanket.

Anyway, the Great Dane on the programme just sat there contentedly with the blanket over his head making no effort to remove it. It could be that he just liked it, but he didn't fare very well in any of the other tests either. Still, if you're that big, who cares how bright you are. The Border Collie romped home first on all the intelligence tests which has given me food for thought with regards to my old rival, Gyp the farm dog. I hate to admit it, but I'm guessing he's pretty smart. I bumped into him this morning for the first time in a while, and, in deference to his likely canine mastermind status, I didn't bark too much and he responded in kind. We even allowed Debbie the farmer, Mr Debbie and 'Them Indoors' to have a little chat. Gyp sidled up to 'Him Indoors' for a quick scratch behind the ears which, not that I'm a jealous kind of dog, was a bit of a cheek. The lanes might belong to Gyp but 'Him Indoors' is definitely mine.

Later in our walk we met the smallest dog in the village who was bouncing along in his normal chipper fashion. I should think he's quite intelligent, he certainly seems it, but I hope no-one throws a blanket over his head – he'd never be seen again.

10TH JULY – PULLING THE WOOL

I'm not one to criticise human kind, after all, most of my nearest and dearest tend towards that disposition, it's just that they can sometimes be quite easily deceived. Now 'Her Indoors' has done her best, but it would be fair to say that I'm not the most reliably obedient dog in the world. I tend to see commands as providing a framework within which to manoeuvre, with any decision about whether or not to oblige, being influenced by that universally pertinent question, 'what's in it for me?'

'Her Indoors' tries to get me to sit at the edge of the pavement and wait for her to give the command before moving off to cross the road, which is all very sensible and worthy. However, if the pavement is wet, cold, or I'm not in the mood, it can take several attempts before I conform, and some mornings we have quite a long argument about it at the road side. Anyway, the other day I was in a good mood because it was sunny, I'd had a nice walk, and there was a child waiting at the crossing. So when 'Her Indoors' asked me to sit, I did so smartly, to attention, with my ears pricked. I waited for the command before setting off and walked briskly at her heel. Once we'd crossed over, the child's mother congratulated 'Her Indoors' on my good behaviour, saying something nice about how good it was to see a well-trained dog. She even let her little boy stroke me which was rather pleasant. I have to say, 'Her Indoors' hid her surprise well and saved her muttering and hollow laugh until we were out of earshot, but I basked in the glow of being 'a good dog', and I suspect 'Her Indoors' enjoyed the reflected glory too. She needs to make the most of it though as I'm sure she realises. I can't promise it'll last.

13TH JULY – GARDEN GAMES

One of the good things about the summer is that both 'Junior Him' and 'Her' generally put in an appearance. Although they're a bit too big to play with me like they did when they were young children, they're still good for the odd game. 'Junior Him' is skilled at playing ball, although sometimes he practices his golf in the back garden and he doesn't appreciate it if I fetch the ball on those occasions. 'Her Indoors' worries about me picking up golf balls in case I swallow them. I've always had a bit of a tendency to swallow small stones, so she's concerned I won't know the difference and something will get stuck. With stones, I like to chew them in an exaggerated fashion that gets 'Her Indoors' all worried, then just as she is entreating me to drop them, I swallow them down. They don't do me any harm – they just pass straight through – but 'Her Indoors' finds it rather disconcerting. You've got to get your pleasures where you can.

'Junior Him' and 'Her' also tend to eat in the garden which opens up a range of possibilities. They are less guarded about putting food down and generally a bit more tolerant of its theft than their parents. Ice cream is usually a good bet as it doesn't matter how carefully you eat it, some inevitably gets dropped. Then they do things like lying on the grass, relaxing, which I like to join in with. I always try and be companionable by lying as close as I can or, ideally on top of the person concerned. I can't say my bonhomie is always appreciated and there are usually mutterings about my shedding fur and stinky breath. It's just as well I'm not easily offended.

Very occasionally we'll have a visitor who smokes but that's not something they do for long in my garden. Because people put cigarettes into their mouths, I'm always worried I'm missing out on something edible and I have been known to steal them from between the very fingers of the unfortunate smoker. I don't inhale, so it's okay, and it's not like I'm addicted or anything – I can give up anytime. Still, 'Her Indoors' is thinking of renting me out to people who are trying to quit. I'd be very effective and I'm a lot more fun than a nicotine patch.

19TH JULY – IT'S SHOW TIME!
Today has been the annual village show which is held on the playing fields, near where we live. They usually put the marquees up the day before so 'Her Indoors' has to keep me on the lead for my walk in the morning, to stop me from weeing on them, which is my usual response to anything new that appears on my patch overnight. There's a big marquee for the vegetable and flower

exhibits, with the domestic crafts being shown in the main hall. There's also a tea tent, a bar tent, and a hog roast so there's plenty of opportunities for the enterprising dog. They have a brass band and I'm not saying they're loud, it's just that we dogs have sensitive hearing. I'd like to join in, given half the chance, but, rather unfairly, I don't think barking is considered a legitimate contributor to the percussion section, so my involvement is actively discouraged by 'Her Indoors'.

And talking of discouragement, in the last few years, they've held a fun dog show which 'Her Indoors' hadn't let me enter in case I disgraced her in front of her friends and neighbours. However, for some reason, today she succumbed and, in a rash moment, entered me for two classes.

Her performance left a bit to be desired if I'm frank. She had no idea of the show-ring protocols, was unsure if the card with the safety pin was for her or for me, was late for my first class as she mistook it for the previous 'dog with the waggiest tail' group, and when we had to trot round the ring together she ran like a complete girl

I, on the other hand, was in my element. I had an admiring audience, treats, and a nice lady who stood at the front and showed lots of interest in me. I was entered for the 'dog with the most appealing eyes' class, which I was well equipped for. As well as having two of them, I engaged the judge in direct eye contact and used the expression that I normally reserve for eliciting treats or getting me out of trouble. It worked: I won. 'Her Indoors' was so surprised she thought I had been shortlisted rather than getting first place. Honestly....

Anyway, by the time we got to the second class, 'best senior', she was beginning to get the hang of it. I had to stop to read the wee-mail and leave a little message in response, but my arthritis wasn't playing up so I didn't limp, and I was pretty lively for the oldest dog in the group. I was pipped to the post by a very worthy senior of nine years, who looked about five, but I took second place. For a dog who has never stepped into the show-ring I thought it was a credible effort and even 'Him Indoors' was impressed. He's started calling me 'Champion the Wonder Dog' and it makes a nice change to have an alternative name that isn't offensive. It just goes to show that you're never too old to try, and succeed, at something new. Now where can I put my rosettes.

And talking of never being too old, 'Her Indoors' had some modest success. She won first prize in the domestic class with her Victoria sponge, for the second year in a row which can't be bad. I notice I haven't been offered a piece though.

'Him Indoors' likes to have a go at the coconut shy. I can't quite see the point. He spends quite a bit of money throwing wooden balls at a row of coconuts and, if he's lucky, he might knock one off and win it. He's always ridiculously pleased when this happens and guards it jealously, in spite of the fact that no-one actually likes coconut, and it is eventually left to go to waste in some forgotten corner, or, at best, put out for the birds in the garden. Perhaps they should have tins of dog meat instead, then I could be duly appreciative of the efforts that go into winning one. Still, I'm just a dog so nobody asks me, which is a pity.

JULY 21ST – UNDERSTANDING ENGLISH

'Her Indoors' arranges adult education classes for a living and, back in the spring, she decided to try to put on dog training classes. She advertised for a tutor and then had to hold some interviews. She was tempted to take me along and make my obedience to any given command one of the success criteria, but she wasn't sure that was fair. Having appointed a tutor, she's struggled to find a venue that doesn't object to the possibility of a few paw prints or perhaps worse on their floor. Apparently the yoga classes and pre-schools aren't keen on sharing their space with dogs. Anyway, one of the things that has come out of the conversations with the experienced dog trainer is that, apparently, we dogs don't understand English.

Well I hate to contradict an expert, but I do. I admit there are certain words that it may appear I don't understand' 'Come', depends on whether I've got anything better to do, 'No', depends on whether the tone is politely prohibitive or one small step from the dogs' home. But there are some words I always show understanding of: 'Tea', even if said very quietly and out of context, 'Walk', ditto, 'Toy/ball', quick, find one, they want to play, 'Bed', a good idea, I could do with a lie down.

The other thing mentioned that I disagree with is the fact that we dogs are only supposed to remember something for a very short time. So for example, if I have a little accident on the kitchen floor, and 'Her Indoors' comes back an hour later, apparently I won't remember what I've done and my guilty reaction will only be a response to 'Her Indoors' being cross. How come then that occasionally 'Her Indoors' doesn't realise that something is amiss until she is alerted by my guilty body language? I try not to give it away, but we know each other too well.

Anyway, I'm not convinced by all this dog training business. I hope 'Her Indoors' isn't planning to take me along. Still, I heard something quite amusing today. Apparently someone telephoned the office to enquire about the course and asked if they had to bring a dog with them! I'm not sure that the college has correctly identified the party in need of instruction here.

The friends and relatives of 'Them Indoors' can be divided into two categories: those who like dogs and those who don't. Funnily enough, we don't see much of the latter, but in the former group are the parents of 'Her Indoors' who've reared a whole family of dog-lovers so must have done something right.

They would like a dog themselves, but they've got a holiday home in France and do lots of travelling so it wouldn't really be a practical arrangement. Anyway, they are always pleased to see me and let me have free rein of the house and garden. They even have some particular toys that they keep in the greenhouse for when I visit which is very considerate. They also have a problem with cats poohing in their gravel and pigeons that sit on the roof, above their back door, and perform a similar function, which makes timing an important consideration when heading out to the garden. Anyway, cats and pigeons are just two of my specialities so I'm always happy to help where I can and my efforts are greatly appreciated.

Like 'Them Indoors', they live in the country and there are lots of great walks with different scents and new dogs. They've even got a couple of Border Terriers in their village, a mother and daughter, who I always greet in a friendly fashion. There is a pub within walking distance that welcomes canine customers and has a bowl of biscuits and some water. I don't even have to pay. 'Her Indoors' is a bit wary of the bowl of biscuits as I could polish the lot off in one go, given half a chance, which probably wouldn't be very polite. Still, it's very sociable to lie close to the table, listening to the idle pub gossip whilst keeping an eye open for dropped food or even better, beer. In the summer you can sit outside in the sunshine, and in the winter there's a nice fire to settle in front of. All villages should have a pub like that.

The other people we used to go and stay with are the younger brother of 'Him Indoors' and his wife. They own my dogs-in-law, Ollie and Archie, of the light-bulb eating fame, so are not bothered by the odd muddy footprint or slopped food. I don't cause them too many problems either!

However, there was a bit of a sticky moment, a few years ago, when they lived quite a distance away. It had been a long car journey, so 'Her Indoors' was careful to take me into the garden for my ablutions before I entered their house. My only excuse was that I was feeling a bit disorientated, but in spite of relieving myself outside, I went straight into the house and cocked my leg on a roll of curtain fabric that was lying on the floor in the hall. Fortunately it was plastic wrapped, but 'Her Indoors' was mortified. There were jokes for years after that about the distinctive yellow/green pattern on their Roman blinds. I can't think what came over me. Still, they've moved a bit closer now, so I can call in and see them as a day visitor which is rather nice.

Clearly those friends and family who are not keen on dogs, don't get visits from me, but if they come to see 'Them Indoors', I'm part of the package. One is an old work colleague of 'Her Indoors' and she rather tends to the view of dogs as unhygienic creatures who spread dirt and pestilence and are not entirely to be trusted. A little harsh but she's got a point I suppose. Anyway, every time she touches me, she feels compelled to wash her hands, which is a little bit trying. However, I did hear a rather good story about her visiting someone who owned a Great Dane. Apparently, this dog had a tendency to drool, so there was an old towel specifically for moping this up, hanging in the kitchen. Apparently, having paid a visit to the house, and received a rather enthusiastic greeting by the dog with a quick lick to the face, the friend retreated to the kitchen to wash her hands and her face, for good measure. The dog's owners arrived in the kitchen just in time to see her fastidiously drying her face with the doggy drool towel. They didn't have the heart to tell her.....

31ST JULY – HEINZ VARIETIES

I was over the playing field this morning, enjoying my daily constitutional with an assortment of my friends and neighbours, when it suddenly struck me what a diverse group of dogs we are. There was Barnie from next door who's a beagle so runs around following scent trails. He's got a bit of a mournful face so 'Her Indoors' reckons he looks like Hector, from a children's TV programme called 'Hector's House', but it was clearly a long time ago as various people have looked puzzled when she mentions it. She's not in the first flush of youth, but her long-term memory is still going strong.

Then, at the other end of the scale, there was the Shih Tzu from up the road, who was trotting around looking like an animated, furry sausage. Dolly, the Highland Terrier from a few doors up with her bushy eyebrows and tufty bits, was also getting a brief airing before her owner went to work. We've even got a rare breed. There's a Sussex Spaniel who seems a friendly sort of chap. He used to have a companion of the same breed but unfortunately the friend passed on a little while back so he's on his own now, which is a bit sad. Anyway, there was a dog for every predilection and lifestyle, just on one playing field, which brings me onto one of the 'pet hates', if you'll excuse the pun, of 'Her Indoors'.

Why do people buy dogs for whom they're eminently unsuited? The advantage of buying a known breed is that you can find out all about them: how big they'll grow, how much exercise and grooming they'll need, their likely temperament, and what role they were historically bred to fulfil. The Kennel Club, and numerous other animal welfare organisations, provide lots of information and occasions where people can meet dogs from many different breeds and chat to their owners. If you buy a first cross mongrel there's no excuse either. Just look at their Mum and Dad. So why do we still get Border Collie owners who don't realise their dog will need a lot of exercise and stimulation, Great Dane owners who haven't quite taken into account the adult size of their pooch (the clue is in the title!), and Dalmatian owners who thought they were cute in the film and hadn't spotted (apologies – couldn't resist) that they were originally carriage dogs so need plenty of walkies!

Get 'Her Indoors' on the topic and she can't stop, and she certainly did plenty of research on me. There's some interesting information out there. Apparently, Border Terriers:

- "will go 'deaf' occasionally and use their own natural instinct and brain" (Pardon – I'll do my own research thanks - Pet Owner's Guide to the Border Terrier by Betty Judge)
- "do appear to train you rather than the other way round" (well someone's got to take the initiative Betty.)
- "sometimes stubborn and strong willed" (surely not Wikipedia!)
- "may chase cats and any other small pets" (My interest in the family Guinea Pigs was entirely altruistic – I'm misunderstood Wikipedia)
- "is notorious for its digging activities" (in the borders of course – thanks www.pets4homes.co.uk)
- "is willing to squeeze through a narrow space to capture any quarry that may be on the other side" (they heard about my 'chicken run' next door at www.dogbreedinfo.com then!)

Anyway, there's clearly no excuse for not knowing what you've let yourself in for. If you want a quiet life with a pet that doesn't require brushing, exercising, or training, buy a goldfish!

Chapter Eight - August

'Them Indoors' have been away for a long weekend and left me home alone. 'Junior Him' didn't go. Visiting historic places of interest doesn't fit in with his teenage ethos so he opted to stay with me. 'Junior Him' did his best but my routine was a bit disrupted. My late night toilet visit to the garden was at 1.30am on one occasion, and involved playing ball which was rather fun actually. Also 'Junior Him' got up especially early to give me breakfast, which was rather touching, and then went back to bed. I didn't get a walk however, I was just let out in the garden, but I did get an update on how Arsenal are playing this year which was a bonus. He clearly recognises my interest in football.

We got a visit from quite a few of 'Junior Him's friends one evening too. They were out on the patio and were quite lively. I expect the neighbours will have worked out that 'Them Indoors' were away. 'Junior Him' made a decent job of clearing up, but 'Her Indoors' still noticed when she got home. She's got the eyes of a hawk and spotted the cigarette butts on the patio and some jelly under my dog bed – very tasty – but all in all, I think she was thankful it was no worse. Anyway, 'Junior Him' remembered to feed me and let me out so there were no barriers to our bit of male bonding. I think our bachelor weekend went rather well.

7TH AUGUST - SKINNY DIPPING

It's been a lovely sunny day, so how did 'Her Indoors' make the most of it, by giving me a bath that's how. One minute I was wandering around the garden minding my own business, the next thing I know I'm tethered to the walnut tree being doused with tepid water from the watering can. It's just as well I hadn't rolled in anything unsavoury, otherwise the water would have been cold – it's her little act of revenge. I was then lathered up with tea tree oil shampoo and rinsed. I was left tied to the tree whilst I dried off, otherwise I tend to go and find something to roll in, to take the smell away, which rather defeats the sinister purpose of the whole process.

'Her Indoors' found my old brush, after a bit of digging around in the garage, and gave me a thorough grooming. We Border Terriers are supposed to have our outer coats hand-stripped, which in reality means pulling it out in tufts, so 'Her Indoors' did a bit of that too. I don't mind as it doesn't hurt and I always work on the basis that any attention is better than no attention. To finish the process off, she de-fleaed me (I knew it was a mistake to let her catch me scratching) as the little blighters tend to proliferate in the warm weather, and stuck my bedding, collar and harness in the washing machine. I don't know what's come over her. Anyway, I now smell like a big girl's blouse and look a bit too well-coiffured for any self-respecting terrier. I'll have to avoid Gyp the farm dog for a few days – the shame. I bet he never has to have a bath.

10TH AUGUST – THINGS THAT GO BUMP IN THE NIGHT

'Them Indoors' don't really understand me.

Normally at night, I go out in the garden last thing, for my necessary ablutions, and then return to my basket in the kitchen, and go to sleep. But every now and then I don't settle. I refuse to go back into my basket and wander around the kitchen, looking miserable. I then sit by the kitchen door and, if left to my own devices, bark intermittently through the night. It drives 'Them Indoors' nuts. 'Her Indoors' is usually reasonably sympathetic the first time she comes to try and settle me, but after that it all goes downhill rapidly. I don't know how she managed when 'Junior Him' and 'Her' were little; she doesn't like her sleep interrupted. I think they always used to shout for 'Him Indoors' and I can't say I blame them. That doesn't work with me of course, because 'Him Indoors' suddenly remembers that he never wanted a dog in the first place, so it's left to 'Her Indoors' to sort me out. Eventually, I usually get moved out in the lobby with my basket, where they can't hear me. I settle down then and go to sleep. There's no point without an audience.

'Them Indoors' have indulged in lots of hypothesizing as to why I do this, when I can go for months settling happily every night. They've blamed windy weather for making noises outside, foxes or animals unknown for frolicking in the garden, indigestion, you name it. They haven't got a clue; as I said, they don't really understand me. I would share the real reason but I don't want to dispel my air of mystery. It's what keeps me interesting.

Anyway, I could do with a little nap. All that nocturnal activity has left me a bit tired.

13TH AUGUST – TOGETHER OR APART?

The holiday season always brings with it the age old dilemma for the concerned dog owner: do you pack your pooch or do you leave them behind? We've tried it all ways.

When 'Junior Him' and 'Her' were little, 'Them Indoors' owned a folding camper which is like a cross between a caravan and a tent. It has the advantage of providing dog-friendly holidays and I had my own little sleeping area in an 'under the bedroom' tent. One night, someone was taking a short cut back from the washing-up area across our pitch, which in my defence, is against the protocols of caravanning, and I was in my quarters, snoozing after the day's excursions. I was too tired to get up and bark properly, so I just stuck my nose out, under the pegged down flaps, and gave a little woof. The woman almost jumped out of her skin. It's just as well caravanning crockery is made out of plastic I can tell you. It's all good fun.

On one holiday we stayed on a campsite near Portsmouth and caught a rather unfortunately named catamaran over to the Isle of Wight, as foot passengers. Having reached the island, we went on an open top bus tour with 'Her Indoors' holding onto me grimly to stop me from jumping out in my enthusiasm. We also went to my first sandy beach which was a complete revelation. I was not only allowed, but positively encouraged, to dig and there was seaweed and an old washed up tennis ball to pick up and play with, plus lots of families with picnics to gate-crash. If there is a heaven for dogs, then it's probably a sandy beach on the Isle of Wight.

Having spent a busy and exciting time at the beach, we caught the train back to the ferry port and I was so exhausted I slept, sprawled in the aisle, snoring. Everyone was very kind and carefully stepped over me, which as 'Her Indoors' pointed out, was more than they would have done if it had been a person sleeping in everyone's way. Still, Britain is supposed to be a nation of dog lovers so it's only right and proper.

Anyway, holidays in the camper were not all good news. The disadvantage of me tagging along, was that it placed some real restrictions on what the family could do and tended to make 'Him Indoors' a bit grumpy. You shouldn't leave dogs in cars or caravans, as they can over heat, and there is an endless list of places dogs are not allowed to go which means someone has to sit outside whilst the rest of the family enjoy themselves.

The alternative is to leave me behind in a suitable hostelry and 'Them Indoors' have tried that too. Now I have to say, I quite enjoy kennels. There is lots going on and I'm allowed to share my vocalising as much as I want without getting told off. There's plenty to eat, regular walks and a paddock to run round in. Some dogs don't like it but I'm not exactly a shrinking violet when it comes to socialising so I find it okay.

A recent variation on holiday accommodation has provided the best solution to date however. I go and stay with a nice lady called Ros, and her family, including her three dogs, all Golden Retrievers. They have a nice big garden so it's a bit of a home from home. I'm allowed free run of the place, and, in spite of 'Her Indoors' giving me a character reference that would have made Ronnie Biggs blush, I still managed to find the opportunity to steal some Marmite on toast that someone carelessly left at small dog height. I'm also allowed to sleep where I choose and it was nice of Ros's son to share his bedroom with me.

Whatever the care arrangement, there's always a considerable guilt factor to exploit whenever I get left somewhere so that 'Them Indoors' can sneak off, unencumbered, to enjoy themselves. When they come back to claim me, there's an emotional reunion and, if I'm lucky a little present. That's how I acquired the warning plaque in French for the garden gate. The fact that 'Him Indoors' had bought me a present should have warned me of what was coming. Bloomin' cheek!

I did hear something intriguing on the holiday front recently though. 'Him and Her Indoors' went to Rome for a long weekend and 'Junior Her' very kindly came home to dog sit. When they came back they were telling 'Junior Her' that apparently small dogs are all the rage on the continent. It's just as well I don't live there, I'm not really sure I'm suitable as fashion accessory material, but I guess I could try. Anyway, it was the report of the flight home that caught my interest. When 'Them Indoors' were queuing air-side, there was a Boston Terrier in front of them, clearly waiting for a flight, although not to Boston. There was also a screaming toddler. 'Him Indoors' was tight-lipped with disapproval, as if he'd never owned either in his life. According to 'Him Indoors', the dog was flatulent but 'Her Indoors' reckoned if it was a choice between the dog or the toddler......They should have taken me, I can do noise and emissions simultaneously. Anyway, the Boston Terrier distracted the toddler and stopped him from crying and 'Him Indoors' is still clutching his silver card and talking about business class. However, as a dog who's experienced many different forms of transport, I see getting on an aeroplane as my next legitimate challenge. 'Him Indoors' better watch out, I could fit in the hand luggage.

17TH AUGUST – DOGGY DOINGS

I've had rather a sociable few days. I've met up with the usual culprits Bouncing Betty the Boxer, living up to her name next to the fence; the smallest dog in the village who I'm thinking of renaming the happiest dog in the village because he's always so chirpy and interested in everything, and Dolly, the Scottish Terrier, who was on the other side of the road so we just barked at each other whilst our owners rolled their eyes and exchanged knowing, terrier-owning glances. I also met Fred, the Sussex Spaniel from up the road who seems a bit lonely since he lost his friend and cohabite. It probably doesn't help that he's a rare breed which must be a bit isolating. Anyway, he followed me around the playing fields, sniffing and weeing companionably. Then there was Douglas, the Old English Sheep Dog from the Barn conversion at the top of the lane. He's an impressive creature. Unlike most of his breed who are kept as pets rather than show dogs, he doesn't have his fur clipped and he's obviously groomed daily because his coat ripples when he walks, like a dog off the TV. Goodness knows why they were used for advertising paint; shampoo would have been a better option. He looks gorgeous. I think 'Her Indoors' was impressed too as she's started muttering about grooming and looking in the garage for my brush again. It's only just over a week since the last session which is rather worrying. I'm a Border Terrier, we're meant to look scruffy.

25TH AUGUST – SAINT ROLO

It's official – I've been a good dog! I'm not quite sure how it happened; I was clearly not paying attention. I went for my normal Sunday morning walk with 'Him and Her Indoors' and I didn't bark at Gyp the sheepdog. Actually, he was engaged in official business, moving the sheep from one field to another, along the lane, so he couldn't allow himself to be distracted otherwise chaos, of the wooly kind, would have ensued. I didn't bark at the sheep either, which was a big temptation. 'Her Indoors' had moved me a safe distance away, to try and reduce that risk, when along came another one of my barking prompts, a big clippy-cloppy horse. 'Her Indoors' groaned audibly and got lots of bribery treats out, but I resisted and didn't bark. After much praising and lots of foody bits, we continued with our walk and met the same horse coming back. I didn't bark at it then either. 'Her Indoors' couldn't believe my good behaviour and muttered something to 'Him Indoors' about getting me checked out at the Vets. I don't think she found our walk very relaxing though and I have to say I was feeling a bit full by the end of it. Still, she needn't worry, it won't last. As I said, I clearly wasn't paying sufficient attention.

27TH AUGUST – WORKING GUESTS

We've had a builder fixing our roof which has been most intriguing. He's been re-pointing the ridge tiles along the top and down the sides, and he just climbs up his ladder and walks across the top of the roof like it's the garden path. It unnerves 'Her Indoors' as she worries about him falling off.

Anyway, he imparted some intriguing information. Apparently the squirrels have been eating our lead flashing. I knew they were up to no good. I've done my best but they always cheat at the crucial moment and disappear up a tree or shin up a fence post. I've tried hurling myself after them, but with the best will in the world, there's only so high a small dog can jump. Still, once they've eaten the lead flashing apparently, it poisons them and they die. They're clearly not eating enough of it then as there are still quite a few of them around.

'Her Indoors' has got an office in the garden where she works and before that was built there was a shed in the same spot. 'Them Indoors' employed builders to take the old shed down and make the base for the new office. I was kept well out of the way which was a shame as I'm sure I could have usefully contributed. I did manage to leave a few paw prints in the damp concrete though. I'd seen a similar idea on the TV in Hollywood. It's just a shame that they built the office over them. Still, it'll give archaeologists something to puzzle over in millennia to come.

Unbeknown to the guys taking the old shed down, there was a wasps' nest between the wall panels. They got part way through ripping it apart when they suddenly departed, running down the garden flapping their hands. I thought it was some kind of game so I barked loudly from the kitchen which I like to think heightened the sense of drama. They didn't get stung too much and 'Her Indoors' helped out with anti-histamine cream, but it did stop work for a bit whilst they bought some suitable insecticide to douse the little blighters with. Still, at least they weren't hornets which was a mercy.

We also regularly have a window cleaner who uses one of those purified water and pole cleaning systems. It's most intriguing. The hose snakes across the garden from the back of his van, which I've investigated thoroughly when 'Her Indoors' wasn't looking. He keeps his water tank and all his cloths and equipment in there, so it's an interesting place to have a rummage. 'Her Indoors' got quite cross the third time she had to pull me out, although the window cleaner didn't seem that bothered. 'Him Indoors' mentioned something hopeful about him perhaps accidentally driving off with me in the back, but he's not going to get rid of me that easily – I know where I belong.

30TH AUGUST – TWEETING DOGS

I've been a blogger for years, if you'll excuse the language. I like to have a medium for communicating directly with my public so I started a while ago and I've got quite a following. 'Junior Him' helped out with the photo – I needed a professional shot to show me at my best, but I have to share the laptop with 'Her Indoors' which is a bit annoying. Anyway, following on from my blog,

I've got a column in a local magazine, where I can air my views to a different cohort of people. I'm a busy, literary dog – what can I tell you.

However, I discovered a little while ago, a different form of communicating, by accident, and now I'm hooked. There's a whole world of tweeting dogs out there, and whilst I initially thought that 140 characters might be a bit restricting, I've quickly learnt the advantages of brevity. There's a select group of Border Terrier Twitter users called the BT Posse, which I'm a member of, and I've got the badge to prove it. In order to join, you've got to have a Twitter account and tweet in your own voice, not by allowing one of your family to tweet on your behalf. The only problem I had was that in order for me to have my own Twitter account, I needed an e-mail address. When I tried to set one up, I was told I couldn't have one as I was too young. Bloomin' cheek. I got round it by giving my age in dog years.

Anyway, it's taken a while to get used to Twitter speak but this is what I've worked out so far:

BT =	Border Terrier, not a well-known supplier of telephone and internet services as I first thought.
BOL =	Bark Out Loud, the canine equivalent of LOL.
Noms =	Food (I had to get 'Junior Her's help with that one as 'Her Indoors' hasn't a clue, bless her).
Zoomin' =	Running around – what we Border Terriers do best.
Sun Puddling =	Lying in patches of sunshine absorbing the heat.
Pawsome =	Initially I thought this was 'handsome', but apparently it means 'awesome'.

Tweet-up =	Meet up: when various members of the BT Posse get together in real life rather than just virtually.
Humums and Hudads =	They'll always be 'Him and Her Indoors' to me.
Furbros and Fursis =	Siblings, actual or adopted, usually of the canine kind.
OTRB =	This took a little while to work out for sure as it's not something you can afford to get wrong, but, as I've mentioned before, it means 'over the rainbow bridge bridge' which is a delicate euphemism for what happens when a Border Terrier stops zooming permanently, and goes to live in the big dog kennel in the sky.

There are various other groups such as 'the Zombie Squad' which is something I'm also a member of. In order to join that, you have to swear allegiance to the cause by making up your own declaration. Mine turned out a bit like a cross between the oath you make before you give evidence in court, the marriage vows, and the Brownie Guide Law. I can't think how that happened! Anyway, this is my version:

Zombie Squad Oath

I do solemnly sincerely and truly declare and affirm that I, Rolo the Border Terrier, will keep the Zombie Squad faith. I will fiercely defend 'Them Indoors' and my collection of rubber balls (including the one thieved from next door) against the unknown evil, often disguised as squirrels, rabbits and crows, or lurking in unfurling carrier bags, garden machinery and things falling out of the tray cupboard in the kitchen. I will bark without obvious cause during the night, and hunt down zombies by sniffing fearlessly and eating whatever I can find, edible or not. Hereto I pledge you my troth.

If you haven't managed to work out what a zombie is, in Twitter terms, then I'm afraid I can't help you, I'm sworn to secrecy.

I also belong to 'Tweet Choir': a Twitter group where assorted pets get together every week and sing by tweeting sections of a song, selected by the group convener, Henry, who also tries to impose order on the proceedings. I usually try and adapt the lyrics to something more suitable which is quite fun. One week I mis-read the song title and thought 'Islands in the Sun' was the Dolly Parton/Kenny Rogers duet, 'Islands in the Stream'. I managed to send all the Border Terriers into a deviation from the planned programme that involved blonde wigs, white stilettos and an ample cleavage! 'Her Indoors', who shares these rehearsals with me, was laughing so much that 'Him Indoors' wanted to know what was amusing her. She tried to explain but 'Him Indoors' clearly thought she'd gone completely bonkers. Still, speaking for myself, I always find sanity an over-rated concept.

chapter Nine - September

The last week or so there's been more than a hint of autumn in the air. Now if I had to choose, autumn would probably be my favourite season. You often get some nice weather, particularly after the children have gone back to school in their winter uniforms, but it doesn't generally get too swelteringly hot. It's also the best time of year for edibles in the garden providing a good opportunity for me to renew my insulating layer before the cold weather sets in.

I'm rather partial to the odd apple or two. Unfortunately, one of the apple trees in the garden died a couple of years ago, and the others were looking a bit elderly and ropey, so 'Him Indoors' removed them too. I'd better watch myself on that score. Still, he replaced them with new ones and this year they've actually got some fruit on them and I can enjoy eating the windfalls again. It's usually a bit of a race to see who can get to them first: me or 'Her Indoors'. She doesn't like me eating them as it tends to give me a bit of a fermentation problem, but I feel duty bound to give it a go.

Then there's the damsons. They're a bit sharp but they're nice and juicy with a piquant crunch in the centre. 'Her Indoors' worries about me eating the stones but she doesn't need to fret, they pass straight through. We've also got the blackberries that grow in the lanes. 'Junior Her' taught me how to pick them myself when I was getting bored once on a blackberrying trip. It's a lesson I've never forgotten and I've perfected the technique over the years. 'Her Indoors' won't pick the ones at the bottom of the bushes as she's worried dogs might have weed on them, so it's not as if I'm taking any that she wants. They're very tasty although they do tend to make my poohs a bit purple and pippy. Then there's also the berries off the laurel bushes in the garden. 'Her Indoors' worries about me eating them as she thinks they might be poisonous but I've been eating them for years without ill effects. She worries too much.

As well as the things I can directly eat, there's the joy of those things I can't, but which attract other wildlife into the garden. The walnut tree is a classic example. 'Her Indoors' has to race the squirrel to the crop. To add insult to injury, the little blighter buries the stolen surplus amongst her plants which doesn't go down very well. She's denied the pleasure of eating them herself and then digs them up, intact but a bit rotten, the following spring. If I get half the chance it's not only the squirrel's nuts that'll get buried I can tell you.

Ah, the joys of autumn, it's enough to make me come over all poetical.

8TH SEPTEMBER – SCHOOL'S BACK

I bumped into lots of children, looking unnaturally clean and tidy in over-grown school uniform, this morning, heading off to start the new school year. I like it when my walk coincides with school time. I think they must have a breakfast club at the local school because they seem to get there quite early. Whatever my faults, I really like children, and they usually really like me because I'm small and not too intimidating. They enjoy the kind of things that I enjoy which is a good feature. When my own 'Junior Him and Her' were little, 'Her Indoors' used to combine my walk with taking them to school and I used to love all the fussing and petting at the school gate. The only problem was when the school bell rang and all the children deserted me, en masse. I tried to go with them but 'Her Indoors' pointed out that although it was a Junior School, she didn't think that junior dogs would be very welcome. I can't think why not. I wasn't impressed so I used to occasionally stage a sit down protest outside the school gate and 'Her Indoors' had to coax me away with treats.

Anyway, the same thing happened this morning. The children were making a fuss of me and then they suddenly departed, leaving me bereft. So I staged a sit down protest which made 'Her Indoors' laugh. They say elephants never forget, well Border Terriers have a pretty good memory too.

15TH SEPTEMBER – ABANDONED!

I've been abandoned! 'Junior Her' has gone to university. This is a serious issue as she is my staunchest supporter and defender in times of trouble. After plotting my acquisition with all the skill of Bruce Reynolds studying the train timetables, she has since stuck by me through thick and thin. True, she gets a bit upset if my terrier nature gets the better of me and I harm anything, particularly if it's cute. And she doesn't like it when I catch and eat Daddy Long Legs or spiders, particularly when I leave their legs poking out from between my teeth. I'd have thought she'd be grateful as she doesn't like them herself. Still, she's an excellent ally and can always be relied upon to put my point of view.

I'm going to have to adjust to her not being here during term time and it won't be easy. My job description is 'family pet' and I'm not sure what my role is now that half of my family has disappeared. 'Them Indoors' are similarly at a bit of a loss. 'Her Indoors' is wandering around aimlessly but she's being very nice to me. I'm probably going to have to turn my attentions to providing some distraction. I suspect I might have to act as a child substitute. Still, I'm sure I'll cope. If I get stuck, I can always get in touch with 'Junior Her' for some advice – thank goodness for Skype and long university holidays. She'll be back again soon.

17TH SEPTEMBER – PLAYING CHICKEN

I'm in trouble again and it's not my fault. 'Her Indoors' should have checked the security of the boundaries and 'Him Indoors' should have fixed the hole in the fence before I had a chance to squeeze through it, into next door's garden. It was unfortunate that the neighbour had decided to let her chickens out for some sunshine on that particular afternoon. The first 'Her Indoors' knew of my little escapade was some alarmed clucking and squawking, then she heard her neighbour's voice calling my name. She quickly put two and two together and tried calling me back, but I was far too busy. She ended up having to squeeze herself through a Border Terrier sized hole in the fence, into next door's garden.

She emerged into chaos of the poultry kind. There were chickens frantically running everywhere, the next door neighbour chasing after me, calling my name, and feathers fluttering around. 'Her Indoors' marched down the garden path with a grimly set face and once she was close enough to make eye contact, she shouted my name so sternly that I stopped dead in my tracks. She scooped me up and gave me such a telling off that my ears wilted. I think even the neighbour felt sorry for me.

Fortunately for the chickens, there were so many of them I didn't know which one to chase, so although feathers were distinctly ruffled, I didn't actually harm any of them. I don't suppose they'll be laying any eggs for a bit though. 'Her Indoors', having deposited me unceremoniously in the kitchen, went round and apologised properly to the neighbour, who was actually very gracious about it. I don't suppose my name will be on the Christmas card this time around though.

'Him Indoors' was immediately dispatched to mend the fence so he wasn't very happy either. Still, as I said, it's not my fault...

19TH SEPTEMBER – PET PROBLEMS

As if my little escapade with the chickens wasn't bad enough, 'Her Indoors' has told the story to all and sundry. Where's her loyalty? The only good thing about it is that I now realise most dogs have transgressed in the poultry department at some point or other. Barnie the Beagle from next door, apparently had a bit of a 'Fenton' moment when he went to a friend's house. He was unwittingly released from the car when the chickens were out, and in spite of his owner's best efforts to retrieve him, with lots of shouting and running around, it was too late. I won't go into the sordid details, but suffice to say, there were casualties.

One of my pals on Twitter also had a little mishap, of the terminal kind, with a chicken. However, on this occasion the chicken had escaped into their garden from a neighbours, the opposite scenario to mine, so what was any self respecting Border Terrier supposed to do?

The result of all of this gossiping is that 'Her Indoors' doesn't feel quite so bad about my adventure. She should have sensed the danger when next door started keeping chickens. I've always had a bit of a thing about big birds - the downfall of many a small male, and I've got previous in the chasing department. That episode with the Mallard in the back border, springs uncomfortably to mind, and then there was the time when we were staying with the brother of 'Him Indoors'. As well as weeing on the curtain fabric and being falsely accused of inciting their dogs, Ollie and Archie, into the river, I also chased their goose. Well strictly speaking it wasn't their goose, it was a wild one that had adopted them, but they had named him which is always a bad sign. Anyway, Bruce was a regular visitor, or at least he was until I arrived. I chased him which was quite exciting as, being a big bird, it took him quite a long time to get airborne which gives hope to a small dog. Bruce did eventually make it into the air but he was so affronted by the lack of hospitality on that particular visit that he didn't come back. It was the end of a beautiful friendship.

Talking of the end of a beautiful friendship, I'm rather surprised I ever got a return invite, but it is to the credit of the brother of 'Him Indoors' and his wife, that they seemed to find my escapades amusing. 'Her Indoors' didn't find her weekend away on that occasion very relaxing though – I can't think why.

21ST SEPTEMBER – FOOTBALL FANATICS

The football season is well under way so 'Junior Him' is rather preoccupied with the fate of Arsenal. The fact that he is away at university doesn't stop 'Junior Him' and 'Him Indoors' having long conversations about it on the telephone. I'm amazed they're not in charge of Arsenal football club. They clearly know all there is to know about running the team and improving their performance. Anyway, a lot of this advice is shouted at the television on match days, and I can never decide whether they really enjoy watching a match or not. There's a lot of angst involved and when it goes wrong 'Junior Him' is in a bad frame of mind for the rest of the day. Still, it's an improvement on when he was a little lad, then if Arsenal lost an important match, he would cry and I had to do my best to console him. If it went well, he used to play football in the garden and I had to watch myself as footballs are quite big, I'm quite small and he wasn't always terribly accurate with his footwork.

Anyway, I notice 'Her Indoors' absents herself from the living room when they're watching a match. I don't think she can stand the tension. She just comes in at the end to celebrate or commiserate, as appropriate, which probably isn't a bad tactic. If the noise gets too loud, I have to join in myself which doesn't go down very well. It's not fair – they're being vocal, so why can't I too? It's one of life's little injustices. Still, if Arsene Wenger needs any advice on running his team, I'd be happy to pass on a few tips.

23RD SEPTEMBER – DIETARY SUPPLEMENTS

'Them Indoors' have got increasingly concerned about my eating habits. I tend to do a lot of help yourself foraging and I'm not too fussy about what I help myself to. This tends to lead to a few problems in the digestive department which can have some unfortunate side effects, that 'Him Indoors' in particular, doesn't have much sympathy with.

Anyway, 'Her Indoors' has decided to change my dog food and has gone over to an organic brand which has a list of things it doesn't include, longer than the list of those it does. It must be on special offer at the supermarket, or I'm guessing that's what she's told 'Him Indoors'. Still, I'm not complaining; it's delicious! In addition, I've also been given vitamin tablets for my joints, and the net effect is I've never felt better and I'm less inclined to find snacks of my own choosing. I've been bouncing around like a spring lamb, which according to one of the labels, is what I've been eating, and I've got so much energy that I think 'Him Indoors' is thinking of changing his own dietary regime. He can't have any of my food or supplements. He's clearly got no idea how much they cost and my need is greater. Just think of what he's saving on the Vet's bills.

25TH SEPTEMBER – BARRIERS TO COMMUNICATION
I've tried hard with 'Them Indoors' over the years, and I think I've got them fairly well trained, but there are moments when there seems to be a bit of a gulf in our mutual understanding. Clearly I don't speak English (a talking dog, don't be ridiculous!) but I understand everything they try to communicate, although of course we dogs are only supposed to recognise a limited number of words so I have to be careful on that front. The trouble is, the same can't be said for them and they often misunderstand me.

Anyway, last night I had a bit of a crisis. I lost my ball behind the freezer which is situated in an alcove in the kitchen. I tried the usual tactic of whimpering and running to the alcove. 'Her Indoors', in fairness, got the general idea and did a brief search around the sides of the freezer. When she couldn't find it instantly however, she gave up and told me to stop being silly as there was clearly nothing there. It took me about an hour, and then I had to squeeze along the side of the freezer and try and get round the back myself, before they finally twigged what was wrong. 'Him Indoors' eventually moved the freezer out so that I could dash in and collect my ball, but the whole sorry saga was frankly exhausting. Honestly, try as you might, you just can't get the staff these days.

I had a puncture when I was out for a walk this morning. Now I'm not one to complain or make a fuss as we Border Terriers are known for our stoical natures, but it was rather painful. One minute I was walking along, minding my own business, and the next I had this sharp pain in my paw and I had to grind to a halt. 'Her Indoors' was pretty good – she's dealt with this kind of crisis before. I was briskly up-ended and my paws examined. She quickly found the offending item: a large thorn, and swiftly removed it. After that, I was back to regular. I was duly grateful but it was a bit undignified. I found myself upside down in her lap, paws skyward, by the side of the busy main road. I'm glad Gyp the farm dog didn't see me. It would have given him a good laugh.

As if that wasn't enough, 'Her Indoors' spotted a puppy and came over all unnecessary which is a bit embarrassing, particularly at her age. We had seen the youngster being walked from a distance, and when we got closer we discovered that not only was it a puppy, but it turned out to be a dark coated Border Terrier. 'Her Indoors' was in seventh heaven. There was a long conversation with the owner about the merits and downsides of our breed, not all of it very flattering I have to tell you, and unnecessary cooing over the junior dog. I noticed however, that very young dogs don't walk, they bounce, a bit like the smallest dog in the village. Perhaps it's a size rather than an age thing. Anyway, instead of taking the shortest route from A to B, they take a circuitous one that involves lots of backwards and forwarding with regular detours. Still, they seem to have plenty of spare energy when they're young. Perhaps they should save a bit for when they get older.

Now we're not really a musical kind of family. In spite of a few painful endeavours, most notably 'Junior Her' with a violin, there hasn't really been any success with musical instruments. And I'm not saying their vocals are tuneless, but let's just say that the singing of 'Them Indoors' has more than a little in common with my own. They do however appreciate and enjoy other people's music. 'Junior Him' likes to listen to rap which is an interesting combination of music and verse. I don't quite understand why they have to point to their genitals when they perform it, but then what do I know, I'm only a dog.

'Her Indoors' listens to most things although she has a worrying penchant for 1980's music which she sings along to heartily, particularly when she's on her own in the car. She does it when I'm with her and even occasionally on walks. She thinks her secret is safe with me, which it is of course, I'm the soul of discretion and my lips are firmly sealed, which is more than can be said for 'Her Indoors'.

'Him Indoors' likes listening to classical music, and usually the first sign of him being up and about at the weekend is classical music wafting gently around the ground floor of the house. 'Junior Her' says it's one of the things that reminds her of home which is rather nice. He also has a strong affiliation to the music of Bruce Springsteen, a liking which he shares with his brother, the owner of Ollie and Archie. The two of them disappear to concerts every now and then, even venturing abroad occasionally, to hear him sing. Now I've made a bit of a study of Bruce Springsteen's music and I think him and me would get along. I'm a dog with working origins, an uncluttered view of life and strong loyalties. I've also got plenty of energy for jumping around, even though I'm passed the first flush of youth. So if he wants a canine bro, I'd like to put myself forward, after all, I'm a dog of the people.

Chapter 10 - October

It was one of those nice, crisp autumnal days which, as Sundays are usually my decent walk day, was rather fortunate. We weren't the only ones out for a brisk walk however; the world and his dog were out there. I even got a very distant sighting of my old enemy, Gyp the farm dog. 'Her Indoors' has a kind of Pavlovian response to sightings of Gyp – she starts telling me off before I've even done anything.

We saw quite a few dogs that I haven't seen before. I imagine they're not local but I'm not parochial and don't hold it against them. There was a black dog with a bad perm and a curly tail. I suspect a touch of Poodle. Then we saw a Giant Schnauzer who seemed quite friendly in a bushy eye-browed, whiskery kind of way. He was walking with a Westie who I haven't seen before either.

I did see a few dogs that I recognised. The Shih Tzu from the barn conversion, was sunning herself in the front garden. I always think Shih Tzus have an unusual appearance; a bit like a composite dog, but she's a friendly and down-to-earth sort. She even roused

101

herself from her sun puddling to come and exchange friendly sniffs and tail wagging. There's none of that territorial nonsense with her.

I also saw Dolly, the Scottish Terrier from round the corner. She's a bit feisty but she's okay if she likes you. She has her fur clipped but they leave a long fringe around the edge so she looks like a piece of Victorian furniture where you can't see the legs. Her fur ripples when she walks so she looks a bit like she's floating. She's always very purposeful and doesn't loiter, sniffing. Anyway, we exchanged a brisk, terrier greeting and then went on our respective ways.

8TH OCTOBER – ARCHIVE REPORTS

'Her Indoors' has been sorting through some old paperwork from when 'Junior Him' and 'Her' were little, when she came across a mock school report that she'd written for me to entertain the family, when I was a young dog. It felt rather strange, reading about my younger self, and it contained a few details I had forgotten, but here it is.

ANNUAL REPORT – ROLO STOCKTON

Personal and Social Development

Rolo is a lively and sociable dog who enjoys the company of others. He has a good circle of friends and responds well to other people's feelings. He finds it difficult to concentrate, particularly when working in large groups, and needs to develop a greater focus. Control of his bodily functions has shown considerable improvement, but the occasional lapses such as on Grandma's footstool, will need to be eliminated if he is to ever be allowed on the carpet. However, Rolo is always cheerful and willing, and does not resent being reprimanded, which is just as well.

English

Rolo is beginning to demonstrate a promising awareness of basic commands such as 'sit', 'down' and 'bed'. He shows an excellent understanding of words such as 'walkies', 'biscuit' and 'doggie dins' and responds clearly to changes in tone of voice. Unfortunately, Rolo's comprehension of terms such as 'no', 'come' and 'heel' is, at best, patchy, and Rolo needs to work hard in these areas if he is to avoid dog training classes. Despite considerable efforts, Rolo continues to defy all efforts to teach him to read, but he has learnt to make his mark with his paw, particularly on the kitchen floor. Well done Rolo!

Mathematics

Rolo has a very hazy concept of numbers and is unable to count, continuing to ask for more biscuits when he has clearly eaten the prescribed number. On a positive note, his time keeping has improved and he is able to distinguish bedtime from waking time, to the considerable relief of other family members.

Science

Rolo is an enthusiastic scientist and has enjoyed testing the chewability and edibility of many items both in the home and garden. However, he needs to pay greater attention to the laws of cause and effect and to show more awareness of personal safety.

Information and Communication Technology

Rolo has quickly developed the ability to spot when a computer is about to be used, and to adopt a range of distraction techniques including playing with his squeaky ball, rolling on his back and looking imploringly at the family member, and, if all else fails, eating his blanket. If these techniques do not succeed he yawns widely, and settles himself on the edge of the carpet for a quick snooze. A very sensible approach, well done Rolo!

Music

Rolo has developed a wide range of vocal responses to different stimuli which I'm sure are greatly appreciated by his neighbours. He has learnt to squeak his squeaky ball with commendable energy and persistence, and to accompany Hazel on her violin with some tasteful singing.

PE

Rolo has very recently developed a talent for jumping and can reach considerable heights when sufficiently motivated. The recent jump at next door's cat when it ventured over the fence was particularly fine and won warm words of appreciation. His jump over the restraining gate at the end of the utility room demonstrated what can be achieved by persistence and ambition. His walking on a lead needs some improvement and Rolo needs to show greater tolerance of his harness if he is to develop in this area.

Other Interests

Rolo is a keen Guinea Pig watcher and has shown a lively interest in Lucy's activities. He is an active gardener and enjoys digging, giving a whole new meaning to the label 'Border Terrier'. He also enjoys sunbathing and sleeping.

Initial Targets for Next Year

1. *To obey commands of 'heel', 'come' and 'no' instantly.*
2. *To have complete control of all bodily excretions including flatulence.*
3. *To have stopped biting other dog's tails when he meets them on walks.*

Comment

Rolo is a loveable, friendly and energetic little dog who has made a valuable contribution to family life in the first seven months of his existence. I'm sure, that with the correct guidance from the dog training manual, he will continue to make great strides, hopefully at his owner's heel.

13TH OCTOBER – ARTY DOGS

'Her Indoors' has been away for the weekend by herself, staying with her parents, and I've been left with 'Him Indoors', who had to stay home because the car was booked in for an MOT and service. Anyway, whilst 'Her Indoors' was away, she went to an art gallery that specialised entirely in artistic representations of dogs. Apparently there was a whole range of paintings, some minutely accurate, some rather sentimental and some more impressionistic. There were oil paintings, some done in acrylics, and watercolours, as well as pencil sketches. 'Her indoors' liked some of the sculptures, particularly one of a dog made entirely from rope, which was rather clever. I personally don't favour anything too realistic. If they want to look at the real thing they've got me. I prefer something that captures character and expression. Anyway, 'Her Indoors' didn't buy anything, much to the relief of 'Him Indoors' as they were rather expensive.

I think I could be something in the world of art. When it's raining and I've got muddy paws, I leave prints in interesting patterns all over the floor. All I need is to transfer that to a piece of paper. I could also splatter a few droplets by having a tactical shake. It'd be worth thousands! I think I'd also make a fine model. Okay, so I'm not very good at sitting still which might be an issue, but I'm prepared to pose without my clothes on for no extra charge which has got to be a start.

15TH OCTOBER – LEAVES THAT LEAVE

After a few sharp frosts, the trees in the village are beginning to lose their leaves. Now I quite enjoy routing around in the fallen ones when I'm on my walks. They have an interesting smell in their own right; earthy and musty, plus they hold onto scents well, making them good for reading wee-mail and catching up with other dogs in the village.

The disadvantage with falling leaves is that you can lose things. My Frisbee, not helped by the fact that it's a faded yellow colour, disappeared for several weeks, and was only found when 'Him Indoors' got his garden vacuum out for a quick tidy up. 'Her Indoors' has tried to help me keep my toys safe. She bought me a plastic trug for the garden to keep them in, next to the back door, and has tried to train me to put them in there, but I've been careful not to master that one. Why would I want to tidy up after myself when I've got 'Her Indoors' to do it for me? I am quite good at taking the toys out and scattering them round the garden though.

The other thing that is easy to lose in a carpet of fallen leaves is my little doings. 'Her Indoors' is always very diligent in the picking-up department. But at this time of year, if you don't keep your eyes firmly fixed on the spot, you lose it, and

'Her Indoors' has occasionally been left standing, empty pooh bag at the ready, bristling with good intent, but unable to find the offending little items. I know where they are of course, but why should I spoil the fun.

19TH OCTOBER – HEDGEROW HARVEST

I've been out blackberrying with 'Them Indoors'. It's not that they're hard up and can't afford to buy their own soft fruit, it's just that they can't resist getting something for free. Anyway, the hedgerows around here are full of them.

It's interesting to consider the different picking techniques of the various family members. 'Junior Him', when he was younger and could be persuaded to participate, always tried to pick as many as possible, as quickly as possible, with scant regard for quality and ripeness, as picking more than anyone else was the primary objective. 'Him Indoors' is also very competitive, so he tries to win on both the quality and quantity fronts. 'Junior Her' isn't competitive but is quite fastidious and doesn't like insects. She therefore has to inspect every berry before she picks it to make sure a) it meets her high quality standard b) it isn't leaking juice which will make it messy, and c) there are no insects, particularly wasps, on the fruit or in the immediate vicinity. I'm not sure it does any good because I don't think wasps take much notice, but she has a tendency to squeal loudly if a wasp gets too close which is a bit unnerving. 'Her Indoors' just picks steadily and is particularly good at spotting luscious berries that everyone else has missed. She is very sharp-eyed, as I know to my cost.

Blackberrying was where I first learnt my 'pick-your-own' technique, so I busy myself with the lower regions of the bushes. I'm the least fussy about quality and I don't mind the odd insect,

I just chew them up well. I find that sticking close to the pickers is a good tactic as they occasionally drop one. It's a shame to let good food go to waste.

Following on from the picking, are the inevitable associated culinary activities. Apple and blackberry pie and crumble are family favourites and 'Her Indoors' occasionally makes bramble jelly. One year she cooked it for too long and it set rather firmly which provided a few challenges in the spreading department. Still, they gamely worked their way through it with most of their fillings still intact. She has also tried making an autumn fruits Panna Cotta, topped with a strained compote of blackberries which was rather up-market. I think she's been watching too many cookery programmes on the TV. Anyway, if she runs out of ideas, she just freezes them. Occasionally she drops one on the floor, enroute from the freezer to a recipe, and I have to say they're quite nice frozen too.

23RD OCTOBER – CRAFTY EMPTY NESTING

'Her Indoors' has bought a book on knitting for your pet dog. I don't know whether to be pleased or alarmed. She's always liked home-crafting and encouraged 'Junior Him and Her' to make things when they were little. Before I arrived, 'Her Indoors' and 'Junior Her' made me a blanket. It consists of knitted squares sewn together and they even had a go at knitting the letters of my name into four of them which was rather sweet, although I couldn't read in those days. It was finished off with a knitted border and a fleecy backing so it's nice and thick and it has always been my favourite blanket.

'Junior Her' also got a kit from Father Christmas one year, where you could decorate your own dog bowl and she painted a ball, a bone and a sausage, with a pleasing sense of priorities, plus a green field and a blue sky with the sun, so that I could eat them in comfort presumably. In spite of it being a ceramic bowl and therefore prone to the unfortunate effects of dropping, knocking or other rough treatment, it has managed to survive, and still performs the very important function of holding my food twice a day.

'Her Indoors' has also made a few things which weren't actually intended for me but which have been quietly commandeered. Take the beanbag in the living room for example. 'Her Indoors' thought it might be a good idea to make a spare seat, out of some left over fabric from various soft furnishing projects in the living and dining rooms. She spent quite a lot of time making an inner liner for it so that the polystyrene balls couldn't escape and then an outer cover with each segment made from different fabric. Although the family do use it occasionally as a seat, it has quickly become mine. It took a while, plus a few mishaps when I slipped off, to master the technique, but I've found it to be the perfect place to sleep of an evening, in the living room. It works best if 'Her Indoors' makes it into a nest shape with a little hollow in the middle, as it's quite a big bean bag and I'm quite a small dog, but once I'm settled it's very comfy as it gives perfect support. It's also positioned opposite the wood burner and next to the TV for uninterrupted viewing. I get quite indignant if anyone else sits on it now.

Anyway, enthused by the arrival of this new book, 'Her Indoors' has had her knitting needles out and I'm now the proud owner of a red knitted bandanna with a beige paw print on it. It was a 'one size' fits all pattern so it's a bit loose round my neck, but other than that it looks very fine and keeps my neck warm, which has got to be a good thing now the weather is turning colder. She's started looking at coat patterns next which should be okay although a bit like knitted bathing costumes from years gone by, I don't think they'd be much good in the wet. I don't want to end up water-logged. 'Him Indoors' just thinks that it's a symptom of empty-nesting and thought my bandanna was quite amusing. He wants to be careful. There's far more knitting patterns for men out there than there are for small dogs and there's only so many things 'Her Indoors' can knit for me.....

27TH OCTOBER – FALL BACK

The clocks went back an hour, which officially marks the end of British Summer Time. 'Them Indoors' complain every time it happens as they don't like the dark evenings. Neither do I. In the summer I really enjoy wandering round the garden with 'Her Indoors', doing the evening plant inspection and watering. Once we get into the autumn and the nights start drawing in, it takes me a while to adjust, and I sit waiting hopefully by the back door for weeks before I finally recognise that winter is on its way and tours of the garden are over for another year.

Anyway, the advantage of the autumn is it always brings the first lighting of the wood burner. We have one in the living room and, to be honest, it's a bit big for the size of the room. When it's really cold it's glorious, but at other times it can get a bit warm and 'Them Indoors' have to open the living room door, and even occasionally the door to the conservatory, to stop us overheating. There's nothing I like better than lying in front of it watching the flames dance and toasting my paws.

31ST OCTOBER – HALLOWEEN HORRORS

Halloween is always a mixed blessing in our household. On the plus side it's the birthday of 'Junior Him' so we usually get a visit which is rather nice. Also, if we're lucky we get small children knocking on the door asking for edibles which 'Her Indoors' has ready just in case. I wish that 'trick or treating' had been a bit more popular when 'Junior Him and Her' were little, as I think I would have been good at it. I can do 'hungry eyes' really well and I usually combine it with holding up a trembling paw for maximum emotional impact.

On the downside there's pumpkin carving. Now I'm not a discerning gourmet, but even I draw the line at raw pumpkin. The flesh is rather pungent and a bit fibrous, whilst the seeds are large and chew resistant. Still, it's quite good fun watching the carving. 'Her Indoors' has got a special tool, a sort of small, double sided, serrated knife. As 'Junior Her and Him' have got older, the designs have got more complicated and this year's was a particular masterpiece with ears, teeth and a long jagged scar. They read too much Harry Potter in their formative years if you ask me.

The other downside with Halloween is the risk of being dressed up in a seasonal costume. Although 'Junior Her' is in other ways the ideal dog owner, she does have a weakness for cute little outfits that make the long suffering canine look a complete t*t! It's only the direct intervention of 'Her Indoors' that has saved me in the past, so I always check carrier bags rather anxiously in the run up to the end of the month. Still, 'Him Indoors' did find an amusing clip on You Tube where someone had dressed their dog up, rather effectively, as a giant spider, and then had him coming out of lifts and crossing car parks. It really made him laugh so I was a bit anxious that I might wake up with an additional four legs one morning. Honestly, the mental torment; does the RSPCA have any idea?

chapter 11 - November

3RD NOVEMBER – THINGS THAT GO BANG IN THE NIGHT

It's that time of year again. My suspicions were aroused by the pile of tree and hedge cuttings that has appeared in the middle of the playing fields over the last couple of weeks. 'Him Indoors' has been doing some pruning in the garden so he's contributed a few off-cuts himself.

I've cocked my leg on the wood pile every morning, along with most of the other dogs in the village, according to the wee-mail. They'll need plenty of petrol to get it going that's for sure.

Anyway, the worst happened and they lit the bonfire last night with the accompanying fireworks. Now I'm not generally of a nervous disposition but I don't like fireworks, which means that I have to bark and try and drown out the noise. 'Them Indoors' are pretty good about it. 'Her Indoors' draws the blind and turns the radio on. Radio Four would normally be my station of choice – I'm an intellectual dog at heart – but all that talking doesn't drown out the sound very well. Classic FM is quite soothing – Bach is a particular favourite of course but the best bet is something loud, with a beat, so 'Her Indoors' usually re-tunes the radio for me and talks to me in a soothing way. If it gets too much, I'm allowed on a lap next to the wood burner, with the TV turned up loud, so it's not all bad.

6TH NOVEMBER – BIRTHDAY PROLIFERATION

This day holds the award for the most birthdays amongst the acquaintance of 'Her Indoors', with a number of her friends celebrating their anniversaries today, a lot of them fellow dog owners. She usually tries to get them appropriate dog cards, with themed jokes, if she can. It's interesting to note that she has surrounded herself with friends who share the same birth-sign as her. They are all Scorpios so not to be messed with. Now whilst I don't really subscribe to all that astrology stuff, I have to say that there's something about that sting-in-the tail that rings true with 'Her Indoors'. She can only be pushed so far, and then watch out, as I've found to my cost.

She also holds onto grudges for a long time I've noticed, as illustrated by the saga of the plant cutting. 'Her Indoors' occasionally takes cuttings in order to propagate plants in the garden. Anyway, she usually takes a lot on the basis that one or two may survive, but she had trouble with one plant and was therefore particularly pleased when one of the cuttings finally took, and started growing. She looked after it carefully and potted it on, moving it outside in the summer, to enjoy the natural light and gentle rain. Which was fine until 'Him Indoors' had an unfortunate mishap with the strimmer. He knew he'd be in trouble so he broke the news to 'Her Indoors' gently, telling her that he'd 'accidentally cut the top off'. Unfortunately for him 'the top' was a euphemism for all the bit above the soil, and although 'Her Indoors' waited in the vain hope that it might shoot from the tiny bit of stem left, it didn't. It just died. I'm not saying she gave 'Him Indoors' a hard time over it. All I can report is that she still mentions it every now and then, many years later. I'm glad it wasn't me, although I'm not sure why he didn't do the school hamster trick and just dash off to the nearest garden centre. She probably would have noticed though and I guess he'd have been in even more trouble. As I said, don't mess with a Scorpio.

Fortunately, I just escaped that particular birth sign, and I'm a Sagittarian instead. Apparently we're larger than life, reckless, free spirited and we don't tend to get on that well with Cancerians, which just happens to be the birth sign of 'Him Indoors'. As I said, I really don't believe in any of it. Now where's 'Her Indoors' magazine, I just want to check on what's happening for me in the following month.

9TH NOVEMBER – COFFEE CREAM

I'm in trouble again and it's not my fault. 'Her Indoors' shouldn't have left the stair gate, which normally confines me to the kitchen, ajar when she disappeared off out this morning. When she returned, she noticed her error, but as I was lying in my basket innocently asleep, she was lulled into a false sense of security. Not for long. First she noticed that the contents of the waste paper basket in the study were strewn around the floor, particularly the empty plastic tray from the first layer of a box of chocolates she got for her birthday. Fearing the worst, she scuttled into the lounge to find the originating confectionary item, which had been irresponsibly left on the floor next to the chair, disembowelled.

In fairness, I hadn't eaten many. Unfortunately, in the absence of the little card contents guide, I'd accidentally picked the coffee cream. What's that all about? Horrible! Still, the fact that I'd been snuffling about in the layer seemed to put 'Her Indoors' off a bit and the whole lot went in the bin. She could have been more concerned. Doesn't she know that chocolate's poisonous to dogs? She did piece together the remnants and concluded that very little had actually been consumed and I was none-the-worse for my exploits. Anyway, I was only saving her from herself. At her age she should be careful about how many of those she eats. A second on the lips, a lifetime on the hips. She should be grateful instead of moaning on at me.

The last time the stair-gate was left open was when 'Junior Her' was back for the weekend a little while ago and she went out with friends on a Friday night. I'm not saying she had too much to drink but she was very affectionate when she came in and kissed me more than is perhaps hygienic, not that I'm complaining of course. She also seemed to have the same trouble I occasionally have these days, in getting up from sitting at floor level with a degree of steadiness and elegance. I didn't know she suffered from arthritis too.

Anyway, having come home rather late, she wandered about making cups of tea, but unfortunately, when she finally retired to her boudoir, she left the stair gate open. I had a nice nocturnal exploration of the house, and, having done the downstairs, decided to venture upstairs, a region from which I'm normally, unreasonably, excluded. 'Him Indoors' was woken up at 1.30am by me appearing in his bedroom. He must have thought he was having a nightmare. He then, rather unjustly, expected me to go back in the kitchen just because he asked me too. No chance! We played a fun game of 'chase the small dog' with 'Him' getting increasingly grumpy, and 'Her Indoors' keeping well out of it, feigning sleep upstairs. Needless-to-say, 'Junior Her' slept unawares throughout the whole thing.

'Him Indoors' is not a good sleeper at the best of times, so this seriously disturbed his night's sleep. The only good thing was that on this occasion, I was in less trouble than 'Junior Her'. As I keep pointing out when these little mishaps happen, it's not my fault.

Today was Remembrance Sunday so we watched the service at the cenotaph on TV. This also means that here will be some new poppy wreaths at the village war memorial on the green tomorrow which I won't be allowed to wee on, out of respect.

I like to remember the canine contributions on this day. There have been a lot of dogs involved in the various wars, and of course, many who are still on active service, sniffing out bombs and playing important roles.

There are a few really famous dogs from various war zones including Sergeant Stubby, who I'm proud to say was of a terrier disposition, and who was actually promoted from a mascot to active service. He apparently saved soldiers from mustard gas, found and comforted the wounded, and once caught an enemy solider by the seat of his pants. Impressive stuff!

Another terrier (not that I'm biased at all), Jack the Airedale, saved the lives of many soldiers in the First World War, by delivering a message for reinforcements when all other lines of communication were cut off. Apparently, that venerable institution for dogs, Battersea Dogs' Home, remembers those brave dogs who fought and died along with their owners in different conflicts over the years, and quite right too. I'm not exactly a shrinking violet myself, but I don't think I could do it. After all, the lawn mower frightens me so much that I try to climb onto the lap of 'Her Indoors' which wouldn't really bode well for a role in a war zone. Still, I do my best as a family pet and although it doesn't win any medals, I still like to flatter myself that I'm a bit of a force for good in a small way.

16TH NOVEMBER – DESERTED

My worst fears were realised. After the little incident with the chocolates, 'Her Indoors' packed her bags and left. I couldn't believe it, after all, what's one little coffee cream between friends? 'Him Indoors' didn't seem unduly concerned as 'Junior Him' came back for the weekend to keep him company, but I was a bit put out. Whilst I love all my family, 'Her Indoors' is my primary carer and the one I rely on for all my day-to-day needs.

Apparently she's gone to a literary conference with her friend and colleague, Danielle. They sent 'Him Indoors' a photograph of themselves in the bar, drinking cocktails. 'Junior Him' retaliated with a photo of a tower, made from the empty beer cans the contents of which, he and 'Him Indoors' had consumed during the course of an evening. All I got was the dregs from the bottom and there wasn't much of that. I think I was the only sober one in my family.

Anyway, to my intense relief, 'Her Indoors' came back this afternoon, full of her weekend away. I was relieved to know that it wasn't that little confectionary incident that tipped the balance. I made sure she knew that I was pleased to see her, just to be on the safe side. I don't want her to get into the habit of disappearing off.

18TH NOVEMBER – ARACHNID ANGST

This autumn, we've had an unusually large number of spiders in the house. Fortunately 'Junior Her' hasn't been around because she hates them. She gets into a state about even the really tiny ones that can barely be seen with the naked eye. 'Her Indoors' deals with them briskly, if they're not too big, but occasionally one comes along that even she finds a bit daunting. Normally she mutters something about their disposal being men's work, and calls for 'Him Indoors', but we had a bit of a crisis the other evening when 'Him Indoors' was out and she found a rather large spider in the bedroom. She didn't like to just leave it, in case it made itself all snugly under the duvet, so in the end, after much dithering, she got a large glass and trapped it, sliding a piece of

117

card underneath and then taking it outside and releasing it into the wild. It was probably enjoying the warm of the house and was surprised to find itself out in the cold, but it was lucky 'Him Indoors' wasn't around. He ignores that thing about 'if you want to live and thrive' and wacks them with a slipper.

23RD NOVEMBER – DOG YEARS

It's my birthday today so that's another year gone by. I like to think I've made good use of it. Now I don't have the same aversion to the advancing of the years as 'Them Indoors'; I see it as an advantage. Over time, my relationship with them has mellowed into mutual understanding and tolerance. I'm allowed to come home early from my walks if the weather is poor, take longer sniffing around and doing my ablutions, and I get a bit of sympathy over any aches and pains. I've also developed a pretty extensive store of knowledge which I deploy tactically, as I do a pretence at diminishing eye sight or hearing, depending on the circumstances.

'Them Indoors' did me proud as usual and 'Him Indoors' was particularly generous in the snacking department which was nice. I got a new cushion for my basket, a ball, and a coat to replace my old one which is getting a bit tatty. I need an extra layer in the colder weather so it'll come in handy. The ball is a blue one which is useful as that's supposed to be a colour we dogs can see. It'll help me find it in the garden. I'm keeping it pretty close by me for now though, just in case.

In addition to the presents I also had a long walk in the sunshine and a sausage for my tea which is a rare treat. Happy days! It's a shame we only get one birthday a year. Perhaps I should be like the queen. I wonder if the corgis get two?

Anyway, it made me think back to when I was a puppy. I came from a breeder in the same county so 'Them Indoors' didn't have to go far to get me. 'Him Indoors' had finally been pestered into submission, but unfortunately, there was a bout of family illness and by the time they got out to view the litter, I was the only one left. I'd been saving myself for the right family. It's not difficult to do. You just have to look a little bit listless when people come to choose and they leave you alone. I was beginning to wonder if I'd been a bit too fussy and left if rather late, but as soon as I saw 'Them Indoors' I knew they were the family for me. I immediately climbed on the lap of 'Junior Him' and started chewing his trouser pocket so that he knew he'd been ear-marked. 'Junior Her' was easy to win over, as was 'Her Indoors'. 'Him Indoors' reckons that the only reason he agreed was because he was in a weakened state due to a bout of flu, but that was it, I had made my selection.

The trip to your new home is always a bit nerve-wracking. It's difficult to judge from a couple of meetings, what the family and their environs are going to be like. I needn't have worried though. 'Them Indoors' lived in a different house then, but their old house had a big, airy kitchen and a utility room that served nicely as my quarters. 'Him Indoors' took a bit of training to begin with, but once I'd managed to take control of my bodily functions, we got on a lot better.

The rest as they say is history and I've been part of their lives ever since. I've helped to bring up 'Junior Him and Her' into the rounded individuals they are today. Even 'Him Indoors' has mellowed a bit over the years, although he'll never truly be a doggy person, he's too fussy.

29TH NOVEMBER – THE DOGS

'Her Indoors' has been busy socialising again. When we used to live in our previous house, we had a regular group of people and dogs that we used to walk with every morning, after we'd dropped 'Junior Him' and 'Her' off at school. As well as the core group, there used to be visitors, and I got to socialise with a whole range of dogs. It gave me a lasting respect for Pugs. To be honest, I'd always imagined they were slightly aloof lap dogs, not given to exercising much, until I met Ivy. She used to stay with one of the group when her owners went on holiday and she was up for anything. She used to throw herself into being one of the pack with great enthusiasm. True, she was a bit small and we had to be careful she didn't get squashed or trodden on when things got a bit lively, but she was always in the thick of things. Her owners always used to apparently comment on how fit and trim she was when they collected her after their holidays. I like to feel we played our part.

One of the regular walkers was a Golden Retriever called Bella. She was the mildest mannered of dogs and as good natured as they come, but she had one bad habit which used to drive her owner, Sue, to despair: she couldn't resist a good muddy puddle for a wallow. Everyone tried to keep an eye on her, but inevitably they got chatting and distracted. On one occasion that sticks in my memory particularly, Bella found a really good puddle and, by the time her owner had hauled her out, she was completely transformed from golden to a chocolate brown colour with just her gentle eyes, peering benevolently out, wondering what all the fuss was about.

Another group member was a Dalmatian called Alice who came along with her owner, another Sue. When she first joined she was every inch the carriage dog and used to look on with horrified disdain when the rest of us scrabbled for biscuits, as if such treats were beneath her. It didn't last. We soon asserted our collective influence and she was jostling for her fair share with the rest of us. I always got on pretty well with her, although to be honest, we made a slightly odd couple to look at.

There was also a nice Labrador, Carla, owned by a lady called Ann, and a Collie cross, Storm, who used to upset her owner, Liza, by continually rolling in that most delightful of scent sources, foxes pooh.

Over the years, several members of the group, including ourselves, moved house, and some of the dogs went 'over the rainbow bridge', so we eventually stopped walking together, but the owners continued to meet up without us. 'Her Indoors' always used to refer to that particular group of friends, rather unimaginatively, as the dog walkers, but she discovered that one of the other group members had abbreviated this to 'the dogs' so that is what they are now called. Anyway, 'Her Indoors' always seems to enjoy herself on the occasion of these little outings, particularly if 'Junior Him' is back from university and can be persuaded into giving her a lift so she can have the odd beverage. She was certainly in a good mood when she came in last night, I can tell you. 'Him Indoors' didn't seem quite so happy though.

30TH NOVEMBER – BLACK DOGS

I heard on the radio this morning that Winston Churchill was born on this day in 1874. I remember 'Junior Him' doing a project on him when he was at primary school and being intrigued to discover that Winston suffered occasionally from a black dog. I wonder who they were? I know a few black dogs and the odd one can be a bit irritating, but no more so than dogs of other colours. After all, that Red Setter from up the road, is, well, red, and he's pretty annoying, whilst Gyp the farm dog is black and white so he's only 50% to blame. Apparently Winston took up painting pictures to help with keeping the black dog at bay, so I'm wondering what he painted; a bath tub perhaps, or the Vet's surgery? He should have gone for a different art form and taken up the violin. 'Junior Her' did that for a few years and it certainly kept me at bay.

Chapter Twelve – December

As a dog of some life experience, if I'm not wrong, the event that closest follows my birthday, is that strange festival with the malevolent twiggy reindeer and the indoor tree, when everyone comes home and eats too much. Whilst this is a fine thing, it takes some preparing for and 'Her Indoors' usually ends up getting a bit stressed.

I'm not sure how it works, but 'Him Indoors' doesn't really seem to play a huge role. He usually orders a present for 'Her Indoors' on-line and then wanders around, dropping big hints and looking all pleased with himself. He's no idea what 'Her Indoors' has bought for everyone, half the time, so he just tries to look knowing rather than surprised, when everyone opens their presents on Christmas Day and thanks him for their gift.

He moans quite a bit about the things he is asked to do such as signing his own name on the Christmas Cards and assisting with putting the tree up. When I was a young dog, I was hopeful that installing a tree in the house meant the provision of an inside loo - what else are trees good for – but I was soon dispossessed of that fantasy. A pity really as it would have saved on those trips outside, late at night, which are necessary, but a bit chilly, at this time of year.

7TH DECEMBER - PRE-CHRISTMAS TENSION

As accurately predicted, it's started. 'Her Indoors' has gained a slightly glazed expression and is wandering round clutching lists, bringing home lots of carrier bags, and internet shopping for all she's worth. 'Him Indoors' has already started grumbling about not spending too much money on presents, and the cost of it all, when the credit card bills haven't even started arriving yet. There have been a few encounters with 'Nice Postman with the Biscuits' and although he's busy, he's never in too much of a hurry to stop and dish out the treats. What a nice man. I hope he gets lots of parcels of his own.

The twiggy reindeer with the evil eye that 'Her Indoors' bought a few years ago and which stands at the bottom of the stairs, out in the hall, has reappeared again. He's just in my line of sight from my basket in the kitchen and I don't like the look of him. He survived a close encounter with the mice in the loft. They gnawed their way through the plastic coverings, but, unfortunately, left him intact. Give me a few minutes in the hall with him and I'll finish the job.

'Her Indoors' has started dressing me in my red coat with the white fur trim again, which doesn't do my canine credibility much good but does endear me to all the local children which is a plus. One year 'Her Indoors' completed the effect by giving me one of those flashing collars that help dogs to be seen in the dark. I looked so much like an animated Christmas decoration walking down the road, that people were slowing down in their cars to take a look at me, and 'Her Indoors' was worried that I'd cause an accident, so the illuminated collar had to go. I bumped into that Red Setter from up the road when I was wearing my Santa coat this morning, and I swear

I caught him grimacing. I can't say as I'm bothered. He's got long flowing hair in wavy lengths so who can take him seriously anyway.

'Her Indoors' spent some time this morning sorting out the outside lights in the frosty sunshine which was rather nice. They're a bit of an effort to put up so she usually does them reasonably early so that we can get the maximum benefit from them. She untangled the set and had to go indoors to switch them on to check they were working, so whilst she had her back turned I had a little chew on the flex. She came out at the wrong moment and caught me in the act, which was rather unfortunate, otherwise I could have blamed the mice in the loft. Anyway, the lights at the end of the chain seem to have stopped working. It's just as well they were low voltage, not that 'Her Indoors' seemed unduly concerned about me. She just practiced a few of my alternative names and gave me a stern telling off. I think she's suffering from that well know seasonal disorder, Pre-Christmas Tension.

11TH DECEMBER - PLUSES AND MINUSES

Well the indoor tree is back and the preparations are reaching a new intensity. I've been a bit neglected over the last week. 'Her Indoors' is a bit more harassed than normal and I've started to experience a decline in my standard of living. The walks have got a bit shorter, and when that occurs regularly, over a week or so, I start to develop a bit of pent up energy. I manage to dissipate it a little through some displacement activities. I found a few spare tissues and shredded them, which upset 'Her Indoors' a little – I can't think why – it was a bit like indoor snow. Then she dropped a few clothes pegs so I had a chew on those. 'Her Indoors' was annoyed. How can you have 'best' pegs – I ask you! Then, with the cold weather, I've started to get a bit more peckish than normal so have been trying to source my own food on walks. 'Her Indoors' gets a bit up-tight about that

124

too; I can't think why. If it makes me sick, she's always very good in the clearing up department, although sympathy is a bit lacking, particularly at this time of year.

Anyway, she finally took the hint and I had a decent walk this morning. I even saw Gyp the farm dog and had a woof at him. I think he might have been taking the mickey due to my Santa coat, but he should know better. It's what distinguishes us dogs of leisure from the working variety, and I know which I prefer to be. Still, a good bark at Gyp did me a power of good. I had to have a little sleep when I got home. I woke up just in time to greet 'Junior Him and Her' who are back from university. It was good to see them again. Christmas can't be that far away.

13TH DECEMBER – FESTIVE FUN

'Her Indoors' had her work Christmas do last night, and crept in rather late having talked 'Junior Him' into giving her and a few friends a lift home. Apparently, he was out with friends too and he offered to give a guy a lift but warned him that he was picking up his Mum and some pals, who may just have had a glass or two. Anyway, I don't know what he said to the poor lad, but apparently he looked terrified and kept apologising if he accidentally brushed against someone. 'Her Indoors' was a bit tired this morning and was grumpy with me when I barked at the birds in the garden over breakfast - can't think why. Where's her Christmas spirit, or did she drink it all last night?

On the plus side, in the last week my Santa coat attracted a lot of attention. We often go out for a walk when the children are arriving for school and I got quite a few pats and favourable comments. I really like children and I think they imagine, because of my coat, that I've got a hot-line to Father Christmas, so I'm getting even more fuss than usual which is nice.

Another plus is the increased use of the woodburner. Me and 'Him Indoors' settle down nicely on the sofa, although 'Her Indoors' got a bit miffed when 'Him Indoors' wanted to watch an arty film which she wasn't very keen on, and then promptly fell asleep. If she tried to turn it off, 'Him Indoors' would wake up just long enough to protest that he was watching it, and then, having secured his viewing, he fell back to sleep. Still, 'Her Indoors' got her own back. She took a photo of us both napping and posted it on Facebook. Apparently we got lots of 'likes'.

14TH DECEMBER – BT POSSE CHRISTMAS CONCERT
Last night was the BT Posse Christmas concert. All the performances were on Twitter and the slots were pre-booked with tickets sold for charity, an official programme and virtual refreshments. I was involved of course. I composed my own version of the Victorian Christmas poem, 'The Night Before Christmas' which I posted on my blog with accompanying photos. I must admit I was quite pleased with it so I'm sharing it again below.

The Night Before Christmas – The Border Terrier Version
'Twas the night before Christmas, when all through the house
Not a creature was stirring, not even a mouse;
The stockings were hung in the kitchen with care,
In hopes that ol' Santa Paws soon would be there;
The juniors were nestled all snug in their beds,
While visions of i-pads danced in their heads,
And 'Her' in her onesie and 'Him' in dressing gown
Had just settled their heads for a winter lie-down,
When out on the lawn there arose such a clatter
I sprang out of my bed to see what was the matter.
Away to the back door I flew like a flash

Squeezed out through the cat flap in one seamless dash.
The moon on the breast of the new-fallen snow,
Gave a lustre of midday to small dogs below,
When what to my wondering eyes did appear,
But a miniature sleigh and eight tiny reindeer,
With a little old driver so lively and twee
I knew in a moment he must be S.P.
More rapid than squirrels his reindeer they came
And he whistled and shouted and called them by name:
"Now Dasher, now Dancer, now Prancer and Vixen,
Come Comet, come Cupid, come Donner and Blitzen."
They ignored all his calling with true BT nature,
But came in a flash when he pulled out the bacon.
As rabbits that before the quick terrier fly
Sent up into heaven, high in the sky,
So up to the housetop the reindeer they flew
With a sleigh full of noms and Santa Paws too.
And then, in a twinkling, I heard on the roof,
The prancing and pawing of each little hoof.
As I squeezed back through the cat flap and into the lounge,
Down the chimney came Santa Paws and bumped on the ground.
He was dressed all in red from his head to his foot,
And his clothes were all tarnished with ashes and soot,
A bundle of toys he had flung on his back
And he looked like the Postman, just opening his pack.
His eyes how they widened, his brow beaded with sweat
At the sight of the homeguard, bristling there on the mat.
But just like the Postman he could make a dog merry
He divided the mince pie, and then shared half the sherry.
He had a broad face and a little round belly,
That looked just like mine, and which shook like a jelly.

He was chubby and plump, a right jolly old elf,
My tail wagged when I saw him in spite of myself.
He saw I was friendly and patted my head,
We shared packets of Wotsits and both were well-fed.
He spoke not a word but went straight to his work,
Filled my sock in the kitchen then turned with a jerk
And laying his finger aside of his nose
And giving a biscuit, up the chimney he rose
He sprang to his sleigh, to his team gave a cuddle
And away they all flew like s*** off a shovel!
But I hear him exclaim, ere he drove off the roof
"BTs are the bestest and that is the truth."

15TH DECEMBER – CHRISTMAS CAROLLING

'Her Indoors' went to the local school Carol Service last night and had a good sing-song, mind you, if her singing in the car when we're out together is anything to go by, I hope she moderated the volume a little, for the sake of the other participants. Anyway, she came home in fine festive fettle. One of the local churches advertises a Christmas service with the added attraction of a live donkey. That sounds intriguing. I wonder what happens if it needs to pooh? If donkeys are anything like the horses that I see out in the lanes, they're quite impressive in that department but it wouldn't really fit in with the festive finery and religious solemnity. I'm almost tempted to go along just to see.

The son of one of 'Her Indoors' friends, went carol singing one year with some friends, trilling out a few lines of 'Away in a Manger' on people's door steps in the hope of getting a donation towards the cost of Christmas. They didn't do that well until the lad had the bright idea of dressing the family Labrador in tinsel and a pair of antlers on a head-band, then they did much better. You've got to admire his entrepreneurial spirit.

'Her Indoors' usually puts one of the CDs of Christmas music in her car, so that she can listen to it when she's driving along. It's not that she particularly enjoys yet another round of 'we wish it could be Christmas every day...', after all, she's been listening to that in the shops since October, it's just that it reminds her that it is a festive time of year and helps her to hang on to her patience and good humour with other road users when she's feeling a bit stressed with half a dozen things to do and no time to do it in.

One of the things 'Them Indoors' miss now the juniors are both grown up, is the Christmas school play. One year 'Junior Him' actually got a good role, as Joseph, and 'Her Indoors' wasn't one of the school governors, a teacher, a member of the support staff, or a prominent person in the school 'Friends'- amazing. Usually they played third shepherd from the right or the sixth angel, and 'Her Indoors' had to do her best with dressing gowns and tea towels, or old white shirts and tinsel, accordingly. One year, when 'Junior Her' was very tiny, she got an important role as one of the sheep. 'Her Indoors' was just about to reach for the cotton wool balls, when a friend offered to lend her a costume that her child had used in a previous year. It was a rather lovely hat and tabard, kitted out of a loopy stitch, with cream ears stitched to the top. 'Junior Her' looked very cute and we've the photos to prove it. It's just as well the costume was borrowed and had to be given back, or I could have seen it coming my way. If I'd gone out for a walk dressed as a sheep, I'd have been in all sorts of trouble with Gyp the farm dog. It doesn't bear thinking about.

23RD DECEMBER – BAKING BONANZA

'Her Indoors' has finished work and, with the house decorated and the presents wrapped, she's indulging in a baking bonanza with 'Junior Her'. Sometimes they work separately but sometimes they bake together which is particularly good fun. They usually play the sort of tacky Christmas music that 'Him Indoors' grumbles about. He's more a Winchester Cathedral choir sort of man himself. Anyway, they sing along happily, often with a glass of something to ease the process, scattering edibles on the floor in a manner that I'm sure Mary Berry would find, quite frankly, rather unprofessional. Having said that, I particularly like it when they make savoury stars as these involve both cheese and nuts, which often manage to escape the confines of the table and find their way in my direction.

There's something about Christmas that brings out the home crafting side of 'Her Indoors'. She bakes when she normally doesn't, she makes her own Christmas crackers, and she crafts little gifts for friends. When the juniors were little, they used to make their own advent calendars at half term. They'd draw the picture for the front and then 'Her Indoors' would choose little pictures, cut out of the previous year's Christmas cards, to go inside the doors. They were rather charming although when he got older 'Junior Him' used to moan that he'd rather have chocolates in his. 'Her Indoors' refused point blank to buy him a chocolate calendar, so one of his uni friends, shocked that he'd had such a deprived childhood, bought him one this year and he sat down and ate the lot in one sitting. 'Junior Her' has pointed out several times that they do advent calendars for dogs with treats behind each door. I wonder what my chances are of getting one; not very good I suspect.

24TH DECEMBER - MY CHRISTMAS ADDRESS TO THE NATION
Well it's almost upon us again. The indoor tree has been decorated, the presents are all wrapped, the Christmas food has arrived, courtesy of Ocado, the baking has been baked and I've played my part by helping with the clearing up and getting under everyone's feet.

I hope Santa Paws visits. I don't want to let the dog out of the bag, but if you've ever wondered how he gets past the canine home guard, all I can say is his tactics are a bit similar to 'Nice Postman with the Biscuits'.

I'd ideally like a new laptop. It's a bit of a nuisance having to share with 'Her Indoors', but as I haven't been a particularly good dog, I think that might be a bit optimistic. Still, I'll settle for a new toy and some edibles.

I'd like to issue a big festive thank you to all my friends, whether dog or human. I'd particularly like to thank Akis for tolerating me eating his treats and rushing past him to Mr Akis, and, of course, I'd like to thank Mr Akis for reliably providing my dietary supplements. On the same note, I'd also like to thank 'Nice Postman with the Biscuits' for reversing years of prejudices.

I'd also like to thank my family for their unfaltering support, except 'Him Indoors' whose appreciation is always rather conditional. Whilst we are on that subject, I'd like to apologise both retrospectively and in advance for my many misdemeanours. I know I'm not reliably well behaved, but let's face it, I am fun and that's got to count for quite a bit in a sometimes rather sober world.

Thank you to all my blog readers. I've had about 500 page views a month! Who'd think so many people would be interested in the everyday life of a small brown dog. This year, I've expanded my literary ambitions into a regular column with a local magazine which has proved good fun and ensured that I reach a whole new readership. I'd like to thank the Editor, Adele, for her sense of humour and for not editing me too much....

I'd also like to thank all my followers and fellow tweeters from the BT posse for their companionship over the last year. We might be restricted to 140 characters per comment, and so far, I haven't got to meet any of them although I'm hoping to tweet-up next year, but

I feel like I belong and that they're my friends, virtual or not.

So to you all, have a great Christmas and make sure you eat and drink too much; I shall certainly try to.

28TH DECEMBER - PAST, PRESENTS AND FUTURE
Well Christmas has been and gone and, to be frank, with all those visitors to greet and bracing Christmas walks, I have to admit I'm rather weary. Late Christmas Eve, I woke up and found that Santa Paws had already been. I tried to open my presents but 'Her Indoors' heard the rustling and confiscated my stocking until a respectable time on Christmas Day. I made short work of the presents when I finally got my paws on them. There was a pleasing selection of toys and edibles, but the squeaky Christmas cracker made out of soft plastic, didn't even last until after breakfast before I had de-squeaked and shredded it. I was disappointed but I think 'Her Indoors' was secretly relieved.

For once this Christmas, my favourite present isn't one of my own. 'Her Indoors' got a pair of socks covered with Border Terriers. What nicer present could she have possibly wished for? Ann, one of her dog walking friends, bought them for her and has risen several notches in my estimation as a result. Perhaps they do a whole range of Border Terrier themed underwear. That'd put 'Him Indoors' off his stride!

'Him Indoors' had his mother to stay and I have to admit she's one of my favourites. She's one of those rare people who's never actually owned a dog but who still seems to truly appreciate canine company which is rather touching. There are other dogs in the family but I like to think I hold a special place.

We had a good Christmas, although I managed to develop an eye infection which has been a bit of a nuisance. Still, it's led to a new party game called 'try and get the drops in the eyes of a small, grumpy dog'. Me and 'Her Indoors' have both ended up growling at each other. 'Him Indoors' has been deployed to assist so he waves a biscuit around whilst 'Her Indoors' tries to catch me off-guard. The occasional drop has actually found its way in, so my eyes are slowly improving. It's all good, wholesome, family fun and beats playing charades.

31ST DECEMBER – PARTY POOPERS

Every year, 'Them Indoors' talk vaguely about 'doing something' on New Year's Eve, and every year they don't. 'Junior Him' and 'Her' are a different matter. 'Junior Her' is off to a party and then sleeping what's left of the night at a friend's house. 'Junior Him' is off to Brighton with some pals and one of their parents is providing a lift back which is good of them. I shall prepare myself for a broken night's sleep, with fireworks, both real and on the TV, to bark at, and various family members coming and going or staying up later than normal, in a half-hearted effort to get into the spirit of things.

I think it's really a case of whether you see New Year as a crisp, blank sheet of paper, upon which it is possible, potentially, to write the future you choose, or a rather scary unknown void, in which anything could happen. I think 'Them Indoors' tend towards the latter which is why they're always a bit subdued. Anyway, life holds no such fears for me, and I embrace the New Year as I embrace everything else in life, as a source of potential opportunities. I suggest you do the same. Happy New Year everybody!

conclusion - The Tail End!

Well, that's my year, or at least one of them, and I hope I've achieved my objective of sharing my particular canine perspective with the wider, book-reading world.

Whilst life isn't perfect, and me and 'Him Indoors' have our regular little disagreements about what is acceptable behaviour and what isn't, I realise I'm a lucky dog with much to be thankful for. I came from a responsible breeder who made sure I had the best possible start in life, 'Them Indoors' have provided me with a loving home, and I'm regularly walked, fed and cared for. And there's been training. 'Them Indoors' have tried their best, bless them, but they're still a work in progress, particularly 'Him Indoors'. Still, we've made some advances over the years and for that I'm suitably grateful.

Having a pet dog, is not always a walk in the park, although a fair amount of that is involved, and requires a considerable commitment over a long period of time. Whilst my own 'Junior Her' bucks the general trend, often the children who clamour for a dog can quickly tire of the walking, playing, training, brushing and general maintenance that a dog requires. The ultimate responsibility, as with most things when you have children, rests with the parents.

We Border Terriers are great dogs, but we can be rather idiosyncratic, with a terriers' view of the world and a mind of our own, which we're apt to vocalise. As 'Her Indoors' is always keen to point out, and 'Him Indoors' is even keener, if you want a pet that won't cost too much, doesn't need to be taken out on walks or kept company, won't bark or doing anything too unsavoury or unhygienic, get a hamster.

Having said all that, we dogs are great. Take a look around you and see us helping to bring up children into responsible adults, providing a source of company for the elderly or lonely, assisting those with particular needs and even visiting the sick in hospital, like my dog-in-law Midge who's recently qualified as a 'Pets As Therapy' dog. Then, although I'm reluctant to admit it as it means acknowledging the contribution of a certain farm dog not a hundred miles away from here, there are the dogs who work for us and with us. Debbie would get very tired indeed if she had to chase her own sheep and a dog is a far better companion than a quad bike, although combining the two sounds like a good idea. I wonder if you can have a basket on the front.

But best of all, we're fun. I don't know what 'Them Indoors' would do for amusement if they didn't have me. I enjoy life. I live in the moment, not worrying too much about the past, future or what others think of me. I forgive 'Them Indoors' their occasional behavioural lapses and I love them in that unconditional way you normally only get from small children, although the provision of the occasional little treat can only help in the affection department. I see opportunities in everything. After all, what is a hole in the fence if not a portal into another world? What is a rough concrete path if not something to scratch your back on? What is a trip to the Vets, a visit from the Postman, or a meeting with a friend, if it's not an opportunity for sharing a few biscuits?

Life is short, even more so if you're a dog, so my mantra is to live life to the full, extract as much pleasure and mischief as possible out of any given situation, bark at those you don't like and cherish those that you do and never pass up an opportunity to eat, drink, have your tummy tickled, and play Frisbee in the sun, preferably not all at once. It's not a bad mission statement, and has stood me in good stead throughout the years. I might not be entirely sane, but then sanity is a relative concept, and is largely just a social construct, so who cares who's barking! Try and look at life from a dogs' perspective and you'll get so much more out of it, so go on, give it a try.

Acknowledgments

There are a few people that I'd like to thank for their help with this book.

Firstly, I'd like to thank my family 'Them Indoors' for their support. They tolerate being exposed to the view of the general public very well, and are remarkably stoical in the face of my gentle exploitation of their peccadilloes. They were also the first fans of my blog although I suspect an ulterior motive for 'Him Indoors'. As he once mentioned darkly, it's a good way for him to find out what's going on in the family.

I'd also like to thank my wider relatives and friends, human and canine, for tolerating my little ways and inspiring my adventures. In particular I'd like to thank anyone who gives me treats, especially 'Nice Postman with the Biscuits', Kevin, for dispelling my prejudices and 'Her Indoors' friend, Danielle Lloyd, for recognising a kindred spirit when she meets one. I'd also like to apologise, unreservedly, to any dog I've taken a dislike to and barked at, unless they've deserved it. I'd also like to point out that all opinions in the book are my own and don't necessarily reflect those of 'Them Indoors'.

My local Vet's surgery deserves a mention for keeping me fit and healthy, managing my arthritis, and supplying treats to smooth the passage of our consultations. Thank you.

On the literary front I'd like to thank Adele Trathan, the Editor of Magnet Magazine, for giving me my regular column. I'd also like to thank all the readers of the magazine and followers of my blog at www.rolotheborderterrier.blogspot.com. Without my loyal fans, I'd be just talking to myself which would clearly be madness.

And talking of madness, I'd like to thank all my virtual friends in Twitter world, with a particularly fond mention for the #BTPosse. Although anyone who tweets as their dog is quite frankly, a bun short of a picnic, they are a lovely, friendly, supportive group and I just wish I'd found them years ago. In particular, I'd like to thank Matthew Joy, one of the founder Posse members and the typist behind Sir Clapton Terrier, for reviewing my book.

I'd like to make a special mention of 'Him Indoors' younger brother, Paul, the owner of Ollie and Archie. He's a kind, tolerant, dog-loving man, but since writing this book he was sadly and prematurely taken from us by cancer and has gone 'over the rainbow bridge bridge'. I send the gentlest of nose bumps to his wife, Ceri, and his juniors, and remember him with great affection.

And finally, I'd like to thank my illustrator, Sally C Greenfield, for her wonderful pictures.

Take a play-bow all of you, you deserve it!

About the Author

Rolo Stockton has been the subject of numerous articles for national dog magazines, blogs at www.rolotheborderterrier.blogspot.com, tweets as @stockton_rolo, and is a columnist for Magnet Magazine.

Helen Stockton is Rolo's owner and he's taught her everything she knows about writing! She's also a writer and creative writing teacher, www.helenstockton.co.uk. She has written a book, Teaching Creative Writing, published be 'How To Books' and trains creative writing teachers. She is a writing mentor and a short story writer for www.cutalongstory.com. She writes for a variety of different national and local magazines and newspapers.